Math Diagnosis and Intervention System 2.0

BOOKLET I: MEASUREMENT, GEOMETRY, DATA ANALYSIS, AND PROBABILITY, GRADES 4–6

Teacher's Pages
Intervention Lessons

Glenview, Illinois • Boston, Massachusetts • Chandler, Arizona • Hoboken, New Jersey

PEARSON

ISBN-13: 978-0-328-86287-0
ISBN-10:   0-328-86287-8

3 16

CONTENTS

MDIS 2.0

Intervention Lesson		Teacher Page	Student Pages

MDIS 2.0

Name _____

Solid Figures

Materials power solids arranged in stations around the room

Find each solid to complete the tables below.

	Solid	Number of Faces	Number of Edges	Number of Vertices	Shapes of Faces
1.	Pyramid	5	8	5	1 square 4 triangles
2.	Rectangular Prism	6	12	8	6 rectangles
3.	Cube	6	12	8	6 squares

Some objects that roll do not have faces, edges, or vertices.

	Solid	Number of Flat Surfaces	Shape of Flat Surfaces
4.	Cone	1	1 circle

I1 (student p. 1)   MDIS 2.0

Name _____

Solid Figures (continued)

	Solid	Number of Flat Surfaces	Shape of Flat Surfaces
5.	Cylinder	2	2 circles
6.	Sphere	0	

Name the solid figure that each object looks like.

7.
sphere

8.
cylinder

9.
rectangle prism

Use the solids in the table above to answer Exercises 10–12.

10. Which solid figure has 2 flat surfaces that are circles?
cylinder

11. Which of the 6 solid figures has 6 rectangular faces?
rectangular prism

12. Which 2 figures have no vertices?
cylinder, sphere

13. **Reasoning** How are the sphere and cone alike?
Sample answer: They both can roll.

I1 (student p. 2)   MDIS 2.0

Objective Students will learn about solid figures.
Vocabulary Cone, cube, cylinder, edge, face, pyramid, rectangular prism, sphere, vertex (vertices)
Materials Power solids arranged in stations around the room

1 Conceptual Development
Use with Exercises 1–6.

In this lesson you will learn about solid figures.

Review the terms *cone, cube, cylinder, edge, face, pyramid, rectangular prism,* and *sphere* as needed. *What is another name for a face?* A flat surface *What is another word for a vertex?* A corner *What is an edge?* Where two faces come together Explain that students will rotate through stations in groups to answer questions about each solid. Have students complete Exercises 1–6.

2 Practice Use with Exercises 7–13.

Remind students to check that each solid matches ALL of the characteristics for that object.

Error Intervention If students have difficulty identifying the faces of a cylinder, find a can and place it on a desktop on one end and then other other to show that it has two faces.

If You Have More Time Have students name some everyday objects that have the shape of the solid figures.

3 Assessment

In this lesson students learned about solid figures. Use the **Quick Check** problem to assess students' understanding.

Quick Check 🌱 **Formative** Assessment

What is the difference between a rectangular prism and a cube? The faces of a rectangular prism are rectangles, and the faces of a cube are squares.

I1   MDIS 2.0

Name ______________________

Lines and Line Segments

Intervention Lesson 12

Materials crayons, markers, or colored pencils

A point is an exact place. It is shown by a very small dot.

1. Color in the circle to show a point.

A *line* is an endless number of points going on forever in two directions. There is no beginning and no end.

2. Color over the points to make a solid line. Color in the two arrows to show the line goes on forever in both directions.

A *line segment* is a part of a line. It has a beginning and an end.

3. Color over the points to make a solid line segment. Color in the points that are shown larger, to show the line segment's beginning and end. These points are called *endpoints*.

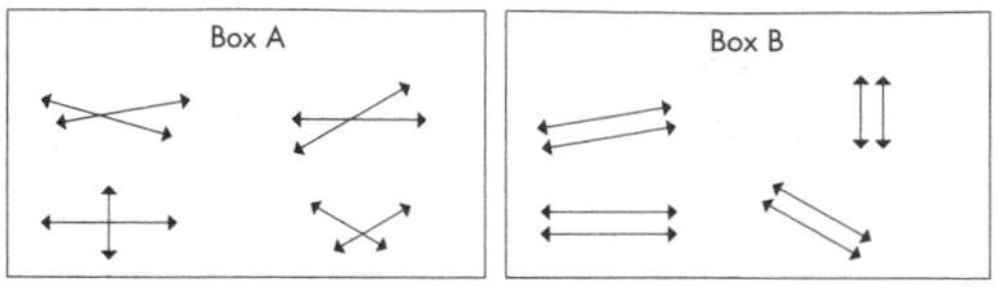

4. **Reasoning** How are the pairs of lines in Box A different from those in Box B?
   Box A lines cross each other, Box B lines do not.

Intersecting lines cross in a point. *Parallel lines* never cross.

5. What type of lines are shown in Box A? intersecting
6. What type of lines are shown in Box B? parallel

Name ______________________

Lines and Line Segments (continued)

Intervention Lesson 12

7. Circle each figure with the color named below.
   points—red lines—blue line segments—green
   pairs of intersecting lines—orange pairs of parallel lines—purple
   Check students' work.

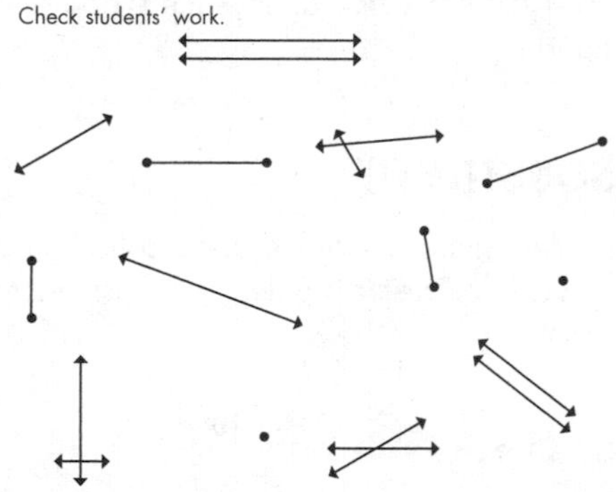

Draw an example of each. Sample answers are shown.

8. parallel lines 9. line segment 10. line

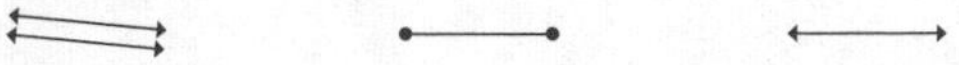

12. **Reasoning** Draw an example of intersecting line segments.
    Sample drawing:

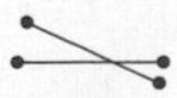

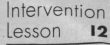

Objective Students will learn about lines and line segments.
Vocabulary Endpoint, intersecting, line segment, parallel, point
Materials Crayons, markers, or colored pencils

1 Conceptual Development

Use with Exercises 1–6.

In this lesson you will learn about lines and line segments.

Revisit the terms *endpoint, intersecting, line segment, parallel,* and *point* as needed. Have students read the sentence at the top of the page. *How can we show a point?* Draw a very small dot Have students read the paragraph above Exercise 2. *How many points make up a line?* An infinite number *Why can't we count them?* Because a line goes on forever and has an endless number of points Discuss how the arrows show that the line goes on forever in each direction. Have students read the paragraph above Exercise 3. *How is a line segment different from a line?* A line segment is part of a line and has a beginning and an end. Have students complete Exercises 1–6.

2 Practice Use with Exercises 7–12.

Remind students that intersecting lines cross each other at a point, while parallel lines never cross.

Error Intervention If students have difficulty noticing the difference between lines and line segments, remind them that the arrows at the end of the lines show that the lines go on indefinitely in each direction.

If You Have More Time Have students find examples of intersecting and parallel lines in the classroom.

3 Assessment

In this lesson students learned about lines and line segments. Use the **Quick Check** problem to assess students' understanding.

Quick Check Formative Assessment

Draw an example of each of the following: a line, a line segment, parallel lines, intersecting lines, a point. Check students' drawings.

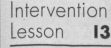

Name _____

Intervention Lesson **13**

Acute, Right, and Obtuse Angles

Materials 1 inch square piece of paper for each student, crayons or markers

A *ray* is part of a line. The endpoint is the beginning of the ray, and the arrow shows it goes on forever.

An *angle* is made by two rays that have the same endpoint. That endpoint is called the *vertex*.

ray

vertex ↘ angle

1. Color each ray of the angle at the right, a different color.
   Check student's coloring

Place a side of your square on one ray, and the corner on the vertex for each angle in 2 to 4.

2. **Reasoning** *Right angles are shown below. What do you notice about the openings of right angles?*

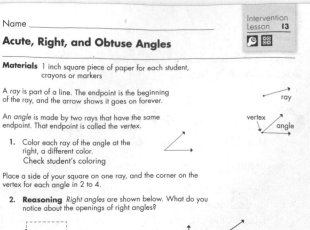

Sample answer: They are the same size as the corner of a piece of paper.

3. **Reasoning** *Obtuse angles are shown below. What do you notice about the openings of obtuse angles?*

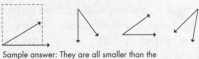

Sample answer: They are all larger than the corner of a piece of paper.

13 (student p. 1)   MDIS 2.0

Name _____

Intervention Lesson **13**

Acute, Right, and Obtuse Angles (continued)

4. **Reasoning** *Acute angles are shown below. What do you notice about the openings of acute angles?*

Sample answer: They are all smaller than the corner of a piece of paper.

Write *ray*, *vertex*, *right angle*, *acute angle*, or *obtuse angle* to name each.

5.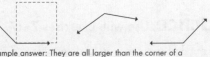

   obtuse angle

6.

   right angle

7.

   acute angle

8.

   vertex

9.

   right angle

10.

    ray

What kind of angle do the hands of each clock show?

11.

    acute angle

12.

    right angle

13.

    obtuse angle

13 (student p. 2)   MDIS 2.0

Objective Students will identify acute, right, and obtuse angles.

Vocabulary Acute angle, angle, obtuse angle, ray, right angle, vertex

Materials 1-inch square piece of paper for each student, crayons or markers

❶ Conceptual Development
Use with Exercises 1–4.

In this lesson you will learn to identify acute, right, and obtuse angles.

Revisit the term *vertex* as needed. Have students read the paragraphs at the top of the page. *How are a ray and an angle related?* Angles are made up of two rays with the same endpoint. Have students read Exercises 2–4. *Is an obtuse angle greater than or less than a right angle?* Greater than *Is an acute angle greater than or less than a right angle?* Less than *Is an obtuse angle greater than or less than an acute angle?* Greater than Have students complete Exercises 1–4.

❷ Practice Use with Exercises 5–13.

Warn students that a right angle can be difficult to identify if it is turned. For example, have students compare the angle in Exercise 9 to a corner of their paper square.

Error Intervention If students have difficulty identifying the angle shown by the hands of a clock, encourage them to compare the angle to a corner of their paper square.

If You Have More Time Have students give examples of two clock times that are right angles, two that are obtuse angles, and two that are acute angles, using the face of a clock in the classroom or those in Exercises 11–13 as models if needed. Check students' answers.

❸ Assessment

In this lesson students learned to identify acute, right, and obtuse angles. Use the **Quick Check** problem to assess students' understanding.

Quick Check Formative Assessment

Show students examples of a ray, a vertex, a right angle, an acute angle, and an obtuse angle. *Identify each by name.* Check students' answers.

13   MDIS 2.0

POLYGONS

Name _____
Polygons

Intervention
Lesson 14

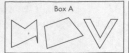
Box A

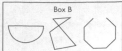
Box B

1. The figures in Box A are polygons. The figures in Box B are not.
   How are the figures in Box A different from those in Box B?
   Answers will vary.

To be a polygon:
- All sides must be made of straight line segments.
- Line segments must only intersect at a vertex.
- The figure must be closed.

Polygons are named by the number of sides each has.
Complete the table.

	Shape	Number of Sides	Number of Vertices	Name
2.		3	3	Triangle
3.		4	4	Quadrilateral
4.		5	5	Pentagon
5.		6	6	Hexagon
6.		8	8	Octagon

14 (student p. 1)   MDIS 2.0

Name _____
Polygons (continued)

Intervention
Lesson 14

Tell if each figure is a polygon. Write *yes* or *no*.

7. ___no___   8. ___yes___   9. ___no___

Name each polygon. Then tell the number of sides and the
number of vertices each polygon has.

10. hexagon; 6, 6   11. pentagon; 5, 5

12. triangle; 3, 3   13. quadrilateral; 4, 4

14. octagon; 8, 8   15. quadrilateral; 4, 4

16. **Reasoning** What is the least number of
    sides a polygon can have?   3 sides

17. **Reasoning** A regular polygon is a polygon
    with all sides the same length. Circle the
    figure on the right that is a regular polygon.

14 (student p. 2)   MDIS 2.0

Objective Students will identify polygons.
Vocabulary Polygon

① Conceptual Development
Use with Exercises 1–6.

In this lesson you will learn to identify polygons.

Have students look at the figures in Boxes A and B
and tell some differences between the two groups.
Discuss the characteristics of *polygons* and have
students count the sides and vertices on each polygon
in the table. *Why is a triangle a polygon?* It has sides
and vertices; it is a closed figure. *Why is a circle not
a polygon?* It does not have sides and vertices. Have
students complete Exercises 1–6.

② Practice Use with Exercises 7–17.

Point out that a quick way to determine if a shape is a
polygon is to look for a curved edge. If a shape has a
curved edge, it cannot be a polygon.

Error Intervention If students have difficulty
identifying whether a figure is a polygon, have them
create a checklist with the three criteria listed on the
first page. Remind students that if a figure does not
meet all three criteria, it is not a polygon.

If You Have More Time Have students solve
the following problem and explain their methods: *I
am a polygon with a greater number of sides than a
quadrilateral and fewer sides than an octagon, and I
have an even number of vertices. What shape am I?*
Sample answer: A hexagon

③ Assessment

In this lesson students learned to identify polygons.
Use the **Quick Check** problem to assess students'
understanding.

Quick Check   Formative Assessment

Which polygon has 5 sides and 5 vertices?
A pentagon

CLASSIFYING TRIANGLES USING SIDES AND ANGLES

Name _____

Intervention Lesson **15**

Classifying Triangles Using Sides and Angles

Materials 2 yards of yarn, scissors, 6 sheets of construction paper, markers for each student and glue

Create a book about triangles by following 1 to 7.

1. Put the pieces of construction paper together and fold them in half to form a book. Punch two holes in the side and use yarn to tie the book together. Write "Triangles" and your name on the cover.

Triangles by Your Name

Each two-page spread will be about one type of triangle. For each two page spread:

- Write the definition on the left page.
- Write the name of the triangle near the top of the right page.
- Create a triangle with yarn pieces and glue the yarn pieces under the name of the triangle to illustrate the triangle.

An equilateral triangle has all sides the same length.

Equilateral triangle

2. Pages 1 and 2 should be about an **equilateral triangle.** This triangle has 3 sides of equal length. So, your 3 yarn pieces should be cut to the same length.

3. Pages 3 and 4 should be about an **isosceles triangle.** This triangles has at least two sides the same length. Cut 2 pieces of yarn the same length and glue them on the page at an angle. Cut and glue a third piece to complete the triangle.

4. Pages 5 and 6 should be about a **scalene triangle.** This triangle has no sides the same length. So your 3 yarn pieces can be cut to different lengths.

5. Pages 7 and 8 should be about a **right triangle.** This triangle has exactly one right angle. Two of your yarn pieces should be placed so that they form a right angle. Cut and glue a third piece to complete the triangle.

15 (student p. 1)   MDIS 2.0

Name _____

Intervention Lesson **15**

Classifying Triangles Using Sides and Angles (continued)

6. Pages 9 and 10 should be about an **obtuse triangle.** This triangle has exactly one obtuse angle. Two pieces of yarn should be placed so that it forms an obtuse angle. Cut and glue down a third yarn piece to complete the triangle.

7. Pages 11 and 12 should be about an **acute triangle.** This triangle has three acute angles. Your 3 yarn pieces should be placed so that no right or obtuse angles are formed.

Tell if each triangle is equilateral, isosceles, or scalene.

8. ____ isosceles

9. ____ scalene

10. ____ equilateral

Tell if each triangle is right, acute, or obtuse.

11. ____ acute

12. ____ obtuse

13. ____ right

14. How many acute angles does an acute triangle have? ____ 3

15. **Reasoning** How many acute angles does a right triangle have? ____ 2

16. Describe this triangle by its sides and by its angles. (Hint: Give it two names.) ____ acute ____ isosceles

15 (student p. 2)   MDIS 2.0

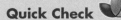

Objective Students will classify triangles using sides and angles.

Vocabulary Acute triangle, equilateral triangle, isosceles triangle, right triangle, scalene triangle, obtuse triangle

Materials 2 yards of yarn, scissors, 6 sheets of construction paper, glue, and markers for each student

① Conceptual Development
Use with Exercises 1–7.

In this lesson you will learn to classify triangles using sides and angles.

Revisit the terms *acute triangle, equilateral triangle, isosceles triangle, right triangle, scalene triangle,* and *obtuse triangle* as needed. Have students read Exercises 1–2. *How will you make an equilateral triangle?* Cut three pieces of yarn to the same length Have students complete Exercises 1–7.

② Practice Use with Exercises 8–16.

Remind students that an acute triangle has three angles that have a measure less than a right angle, and an obtuse triangle has one angle that is greater than a right angle.

Error Intervention If students have difficulty determining whether a triangle is equilateral, isosceles, or scalene, suggest than they use yarn to measure the sides to see if they are of equal length.

If You Have More Time Have students write the definition of each triangle on a note card and the name of the triangle on another card. Ask them to shuffle the definition cards and the triangle name cards, draw one of each, and match the triangle with its definition. Check students' work.

③ Assessment

In this lesson students learned to classify triangles using sides and angles. Use the **Quick Check** problem to assess students' understanding.

Quick Check   🌿 Formative Assessment

Show students an example of each type of triangle. *Identify each triangle.* Check students' answers.

Student Worksheet (Page 1)

Name _____

Quadrilaterals

Intervention Lesson **16**

Materials Have quadrilateral power shapes available for students who want to use them.

For 1 to 5 study each quadrilateral with your partner. Identify the types of angles. Compare the lengths of the sides. Then draw a line to match the quadrilateral with the best description. Descriptions can be used only once.

1. Trapezoid

2. Parallelogram

3. Rectangle

4. Square

5. Rhombus

Four right angles and all four sides the same length

All sides are the same length

Exactly one pair of parallel sides

Two pairs of parallel sides

Four right angles and opposite sides the same length

6. **Reasoning** What quadrilateral has four right angles and opposite sides the same length, and can also be called a rectangle?   square

7. **Reasoning** What quadrilaterals have two pairs of parallel sides, and can also be called parallelograms?

_____ rectangle, rhombus, square

16 (student p. 1)   MDIS 2.0

Student Worksheet (Page 2)

Name _____

Quadrilaterals (continued)

Intervention Lesson **16**

For Exercises 8–13, circle squares red, rectangles blue, parallelograms green, rhombuses orange and trapezoids purple. Some quadrilaterals may be circled more than once. See teachers note page.

8.   9.   10.

11.   12.   13.

14. I have two pairs of parallel sides, and all of my sides are equal, but I have no right angles. What quadrilateral am I?   rhombus

15. I have two pairs of parallel sides and 4 right angles, but all 4 of my sides are not equal. What quadrilateral am I?   rectangle

16. Name all of the quadrilaterals in the picture at the right.
rectangle, rhombus, parallogram, trapezoid

17. **Reasoning** Why is the quadrilateral on the right a parallelogram, but not a rectangle?
Sample answer: Both a rectangle and a parallelogram have opposite sides parallel. A rectangle must also have four right angles. This quadrilateral does not have four right angles, so it is a parallelogram, but not a rectangle.

16 (student p. 2)   MDIS 2.0

Teacher Notes

Objective Students will identify quadrilaterals.
Vocabulary Quadrilateral
Materials Quadrilateral power shapes

❶ Conceptual Development
Use with Exercises 1–7.

In this lesson you will learn to identify quadrilaterals.

Read the paragraph at the top of the page aloud. Revisit the term *quadrilateral* as needed. Have students work with a partner to match each quadrilateral with the best description. *Look at the trapezoid. Which of the listed descriptions matches the trapezoid best?* Exactly one pair of parallel sides *Could any of the other descriptions match the trapezoid? Explain.* No; Sample answer: For example, if a trapezoid had two pairs of parallel sides, it would look like a parallelogram. Have students complete Exercises 1–7.

❷ Practice Use with Exercises 8–17.

Point out that one shape can be more than one type of quadrilateral. For example, a rectangle is also a parallelogram.

Error Intervention If students have difficulty identifying quadrilaterals, encourage them to compare the figures to those on the previous page and use the definitions and figures to help confirm their responses.

If You Have More Time Have students create riddles about quadrilaterals and share them with a partner. For example: *I have four right angles. My opposite sides are the same length. What am I?* Sample answer: A rectangle

❸ Assessment

In this lesson students learned to identify quadrilaterals. Use the **Quick Check** problem to assess students' understanding.

Quick Check 🌿 Formative Assessment

A square is also what three other types of quadrilateral? Parallelogram, rectangle, rhombus

---

Name _____

Making New Shapes from Shapes

Intervention
Lesson 17

Use rhombus pattern blocks to make 1 and 2. Draw the blocks you used.

1.

2.
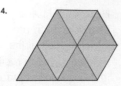

Use triangle pattern blocks to make 3 and 4. Draw the blocks you used.

3.

4.
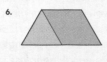

Use triangle and rhombus pattern blocks to make 5 and 6. Draw the blocks you used.

5.
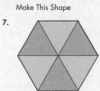

6.

17 (student p. 1)   MDIS 2.0

Name _____

Making New Shapes from Shapes (continued)

Intervention
Lesson 17

Use pattern blocks to make each shape.
Draw the blocks you used.

Make This Shape   Use These Shapes

7.

8.

9.
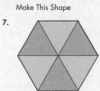
and

Sample answer is shown.

10. Create your own shape.
Show the blocks you used.

17 (student p. 2)   MDIS 2.0

Objective Students will learn to make new shapes
from shapes.
Materials Pattern blocks: 2 hexagons,
2 trapezoids, 1 parallelogram, 3 rhombuses, and
7 triangles for each student, pair, or group

① Conceptual Development
Use with Exercises 1–6.

*In this lesson you will learn to make new shapes from
shapes.*

Display each pattern block and ask students to identify
the shape. *Look at the shape in Exercise 1. Using the
rhombus pattern blocks, can you cover this shape
completely? Explain.* Yes; I can use 3 rhombuses
to cover the shape completely. *Using the triangle
pattern blocks, can you cover this shape completely?
Explain.* Yes; I can use 6 triangles to cover the shape
completely. Have students complete Exercises 2–6.

② Practice Use with Exercises 7–10.

When students are covering a shape with the pattern
blocks, tell them to begin at the edge of the shape, not
in the middle.

Error Intervention If students have difficulty
making the shape in Exercise 9, encourage students to
begin by putting one parallelogram pattern block and
one triangle pattern block together to see what shape
the two shapes make.

If You Have More Time Have students
create another shape with pattern blocks, trace it, note
the shapes they used, and then have a partner make
the shape. Check students' work.

③ Assessment

In this lesson students learned to make new shapes
from shapes. Use the **Quick Check** problem to
assess students' understanding.

Quick Check **Formative**
Assessment

*What shapes could you use to make one large
triangle?* Sample answer: 1 rhombus and 7 triangles

Worksheet (student p. 1)

Name _____

Cutting Shapes Apart

Intervention
Lesson **18**

For Exercise 1, draw 1 line to make 2 squares. For Exercise 2, draw 1 line to make 2 rectangles.

1.

2.

For Exercise 3, draw 1 line to make 2 triangles. For Exercise 4, draw 2 lines to make 4 triangles.

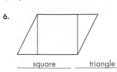

3.

4.

Sample answers are shown.

For Exercises 5 and 6, draw 2 lines to cut the parallelogram into smaller shapes two different ways. List the shapes you made.

5.   ___triangle___ _____

6.   ___square___ ___triangle___

For Exercises 7 and 8, draw 3 lines to cut the hexagon into smaller shapes two different ways. List the shapes you made.

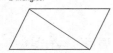

7.   ___triangle___ _____

8.   ___rectangle___ ___triangle___

18 (student p. 1)   MDIS 2.0

Worksheet (student p. 2)

Name _____

Cutting Shapes Apart (continued)

Intervention
Lesson **18**

Draw lines to make new shapes. Sample answers shown.

9. Draw 1 line to make 2 triangles.

10. Draw 2 lines to make 4 squares.

11. Draw 3 lines to make 6 rectangles.

12. Draw 3 lines to make 6 triangles.

Draw the number of lines shown to make new shapes. Write the names of the shapes you made.

13. 1 line

   ___triangle___

14. 2 lines

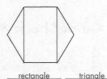

   ___rectangle___ ___triangle___

18 (student p. 2)   MDIS 2.0

Objective Students will cut shapes apart.
Materials Ruler or straightedge for each student, crayons or markers

1 Conceptual Development
Use with Exercises 1–8.

In this lesson you will learn to cut shapes apart.

Have students identify each of the shapes in Exercises 1, 5, and 7. Allow students time to work through each of the following questions with a partner. *Can the rectangle in Exercise 1 be divided into two equal squares? Explain.* Yes; I can divide it by drawing a line vertically and passing through the center of the rectangle. *Can it be divided into two equal rectangles? Explain.* Yes; I can divide it by drawing a line horizontally and passing through the center of the rectangle. *How would you divide it into two equal triangles?* I can draw a line diagonally across the rectangle. Have students complete the remaining exercises.

2 Practice Use with Exercises 9–14.

Point out that there might be more than one correct solution to an exercise. For example, there are two ways to cut a parallelogram with one line to make two triangles.

Error Intervention If students have difficulty drawing lines to create new shapes, encourage them to experiment and use spaghetti to divide the shapes before they draw the lines.

If You Have More Time Have students draw lines to divide a triangle into three triangles and a rectangle. Check students' drawings.

3 Assessment

In this lesson students learned to cut shapes apart. Use the **Quick Check** problem to assess students' understanding.

Quick Check **Formative** Assessment

Begin with a square. Show how to draw two lines to make four squares. Check students' drawings.

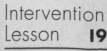
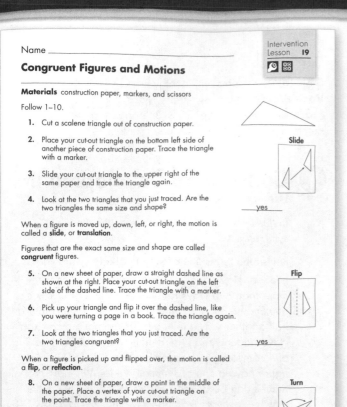

Name _____

Congruent Figures and Motions

Intervention
Lesson 19

Materials construction paper, markers, and scissors

Follow 1–10.

1. Cut a scalene triangle out of construction paper.

2. Place your cut-out triangle on the bottom left side of another piece of construction paper. Trace the triangle with a marker.

3. Slide your cut-out triangle to the upper right of the same paper and trace the triangle again.

4. Look at the two triangles that you just traced. Are the two triangles the same size and shape? _____yes_____

Slide

When a figure is moved up, down, left, or right, the motion is called a **slide**, or **translation**.

Figures that are the exact same size and shape are called **congruent** figures.

5. On a new sheet of paper, draw a straight dashed line as shown at the right. Place your cut-out triangle on the left side of the dashed line. Trace the triangle with a marker.

Flip

6. Pick up your triangle and flip it over the dashed line, like you were turning a page in a book. Trace the triangle again.

7. Look at the two triangles that you just traced. Are the two triangles congruent? _____yes_____

When a figure is picked up and flipped over, the motion is called a **flip**, or **reflection**.

8. On a new sheet of paper, draw a point in the middle of the paper. Place a vertex of your cut-out triangle on the point. Trace the triangle with a marker.

Turn

9. Keep the vertex of your triangle on the point and move the triangle around the point like the hands on a clock. Trace the triangle again.

19 (student p. 1)　　MDIS 2.0

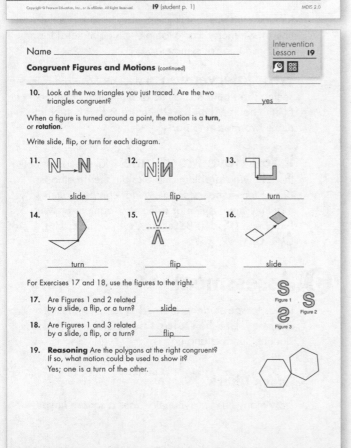

Name _____

Congruent Figures and Motions (continued)

Intervention
Lesson 19

10. Look at the two triangles you just traced. Are the two triangles congruent? _____yes_____

When a figure is turned around a point, the motion is a **turn**, or **rotation**.

Write slide, flip, or turn for each diagram.

11.　N→N　　12.　NИ　　13. ⌐⌐
　　_____slide_____　　_____flip_____　　_____turn_____

14.　　　　15. V̄V̄　　16.
　　_____turn_____　　_____flip_____　　_____slide_____

For Exercises 17 and 18, use the figures to the right.

17. Are Figures 1 and 2 related by a slide, a flip, or a turn? _____slide_____

18. Are Figures 1 and 3 related by a slide, a flip, or a turn? _____flip_____

Figure 1　S
Figure 2　S
Figure 3　S

19. **Reasoning** Are the polygons at the right congruent? If so, what motion could be used to show it?
Yes; one is a turn of the other.

19 (student p. 2)　　MDIS 2.0

Objective Students will learn about congruent figures and motions.
Vocabulary Congruent, flip, reflection, rotation, slide, turn, translation
Materials Construction paper, markers, and scissors

① Conceptual Development
Use with Exercises 1–10.

In this lesson you will learn about congruent figures and motions.

Revisit the terms *flip, reflection, rotation, slide, turn,* and *translation* as needed. Have students follow the steps in Exercises 1–4. *When you slide a figure, do the size and shape of the figure change?* No *What changes?* Its location Tell students that figures that are the same size and shape are *congruent.* Explain that shapes can be moved in different ways without changing the size and shape. Have students complete Exercises 5–10.

② Practice Use with Exercises 11–19.

Suggest that students review the three motions by cutting out a new shape and practice sliding, flipping, and turning it.

Error Intervention If students have difficulty remembering the terms, have them write *slide, flip,* and *turn* on a sheet of paper and draw an example beside each.

If You Have More Time Have students draw examples of a slide, a turn, and a flip and exchange them with a partner to identify. Check students' work.

③ Assessment

In this lesson students learned about congruent figures and motions. Use the **Quick Check** problem to assess students' understanding.

Quick Check 　Formative Assessment

What are congruent figures? Figures that are the same size and shape

Name _____

Line Symmetry

Materials one sheet of 3" × 3" paper, two sheets of 2" × 4" paper, for each student

1. How many ways can you fold a rectangular sheet of paper so that the two parts match exactly?

_2_

A **line of symmetry** is a line on which a figure can be folded so the two parts match exactly.

2. Fold the square sheet of paper as many ways as you can so the two sides match. One way is shown at the right. How many lines of symmetry does a square have? _4_

3. Cut a rectangular sheet of paper in half as shown at the right. Cut out one of the triangles formed.

4. Fold the right triangle as many ways as you can so two sides match. How many lines of symmetry does the right triangle have? _0_

If a figure has at least one line of symmetry, it is **symmetric**.

5. Circle the figures that are symmetric.

To draw a symmetric figure, flip the given half over the line of symmetry.

110 (student p. 1)   MDIS 2.0

Name _____

Line Symmetry (continued)

Complete the figure below to make a symmetric figure by answering 6 to 8.

6. Find a vertex that is not on the line of symmetry. Count the number of spaces from the line of symmetry to the vertex.

7. Count the same number of spaces on the other side of the line of symmetry and mark a point.

8. Use line segments to connect the new vertices. Do this until the figure is complete.

line of symmetry

2 spaces 2 spaces

Decide whether or not each figure is symmetric. Write Yes or No.

9.

10.

11.

_____yes_____   _____yes_____   _____no_____

Complete each figure so the dotted line segment is the line of symmetry.

12.   13.

Draw all lines of symmetry for each figure.

14.   15.

110 (student p. 2)   MDIS 2.0

Objective Students will identify lines of symmetry.
Vocabulary Line of symmetry, symmetric
Materials one sheet of 3" × 3" paper and two sheets of 2" × 4" paper, for each student

1 Conceptual Development
Use with Exercises 1–8.

In this lesson you will learn to identify lines of symmetry.

Revisit the terms *line of symmetry* and *symmetric* as needed. Have students read Exercise 1. *Are there more than two ways to fold the paper?* No *How do you know?* Because when I tried to fold the paper in half another way, the two parts did not match exactly. Have students read the definition below Exercise 1 and complete the steps in Exercises 2–4. *Does every figure have a line of symmetry?* No *Why not?* Not all figures can be divided in half so that the two sides match exactly. Have students complete Exercises 5–8.

2 Practice Use with Exercises 9–15.

Remind students that a shape can have more than one line of symmetry. For example, an equilateral triangle has three lines of symmetry.

Error Intervention If students have difficulty seeing if a figure has a line of symmetry, have them cut out the figure. Then have them try to fold it in half to make two matching parts.

If You Have More Time Have students solve the following problem and explain their methods: *Name ten numbers or letters that can be written so that they have a line of symmetry.* Sample answers: Numbers: 0, 1, 3, 8; Letters: A, B, C, D, E, H, I, K, M, O, T, U, V, W, X, Y

3 Assessment

In this lesson students learned to identify lines of symmetry. Use the **Quick Check** problem to assess students' understanding.

Quick Check **Formative** Assessment

How many lines of symmetry does a square have? 4

SOLIDS AND NETS

Name _____

Solids and Nets

Materials tape, scissors, copy of nets for all prisms, square and rectangular pyramids from *Teaching Tool Masters*

Cut out and tape each net to help complete the tables. Each group should make 7 solids.

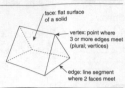

face: flat surface of a solid
vertex: point where 3 or more edges meet (plural; vertices)
edge: line segment where 2 faces meet

	Solid	Faces	Edges	Vertices	Shapes of Faces
1.	Pyramid	5	8	5	1 square / 4 triangles
2.	Rectangular Pyramid	5	8	5	1 rectangle, 4 triangles
3.	Cube	6	12	8	6 squares
4.	Rectangular Prism	6	12	8	6 rectangles
5.	Triangular Prism	5	9	6	2 triangles, 3 rectangles

111 (student p. 1)   MDIS 2.0

Name _____

Solids and Nets (continued)

What solid will each net form?

6.
cylinder

7.
cube

8.
rectangular prism

9.
triangular prism

10.
cone

11.
square pyramid

12. **Reasoning** Is the figure a net for a cube? Explain.

No; the net only has five faces and a cube has six faces.

111 (student p. 2)   MDIS 2.0

Objective Students will learn about solids and nets.

Vocabulary Cube, edge, face, pyramid, rectangular prism, rectangular pyramid, triangular prism, vertex (vertices)

Materials Tape, scissors, copy of nets for all prisms, square and rectangular prisms from *Teaching Tool Masters*

❶ Conceptual Development
Use with Exercises 1–5.

In this lesson you will learn about solids and nets.

Revisit the terms *cube*, *edge*, *face*, *pyramid*, *rectangular prism*, *rectangular pyramid*, *triangular prism*, and *vertex (vertices)* as needed. Display and discuss each net before students cut it out. Count the faces, edges, and vertices of each solid together. *What is the shape of each face of a cube?* A square *How many of the faces of a triangular prism are triangles?* 2 Have students complete Exercises 1–5.

❷ Practice Use with Exercises 6–12.

Suggest that students look at each net and think about a solid that has the faces shown in the net.

Error Intervention If students have difficulty identifying solids, extend the table to include the two nets not in the table.

If You Have More Time Have students explain how they know that a square pyramid and a rectangular pyramid have the same number of faces, edges, and vertices. Since a square is also a rectangle, a square pyramid is also a rectangular pyramid.

❸ Assessment

In this lesson students learned about solids and nets. Use the **Quick Check** problem to assess students' understanding.

Quick Check Formative Assessment

Display a triangular prism. *Name the solid using the chart. How many faces, edges, and vertices does it have.* Triangular prism; 5 faces; 9 edges; 6 vertices

111 MDIS 2.0

VIEWS OF SOLID FIGURES

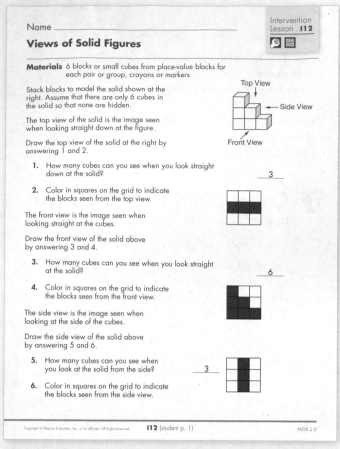

Name _____

Views of Solid Figures

Materials 6 blocks or small cubes from place-value blocks for each pair or group, crayons or markers

Stack blocks to model the solid shown at the right. Assume that there are only 6 cubes in the solid so that none are hidden.

The top view of the solid is the image seen when looking straight down at the figure.

Draw the top view of the solid at the right by answering 1 and 2.

1. How many cubes can you see when you look straight down at the solid? _____3_____

2. Color in squares on the grid to indicate the blocks seen from the top view.

The front view is the image seen when looking straight at the cubes.

Draw the front view of the solid above by answering 3 and 4.

3. How many cubes can you see when you look straight at the solid? _____6_____

4. Color in squares on the grid to indicate the blocks seen from the front view.

The side view is the image seen when looking at the side of the cubes.

Draw the side view of the solid above by answering 5 and 6.

5. How many cubes can you see when you look at the solid from the side? _____3_____

6. Color in squares on the grid to indicate the blocks seen from the side view.

112 (student p. 1)   MDIS 2.0

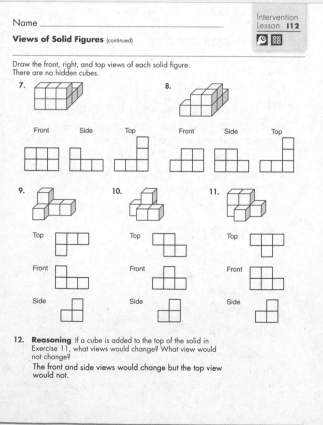

Name _____

Views of Solid Figures (continued)

Draw the front, right, and top views of each solid figure. There are no hidden cubes.

7.   Front   Side   Top

8.   Front   Side   Top

9.   Top   Front   Side

10.   Top   Front   Side

11.   Top   Front   Side

12. **Reasoning** If a cube is added to the top of the solid in Exercise 11, what views would change? What view would not change?
The front and side views would change but the top view would not.

112 (student p. 2)   MDIS 2.0

Objective Students will learn about views of solid figures.

Materials 6 blocks or small cubes from place-value blocks for each pair or group, crayons or markers

1 Conceptual Development
Use with Exercises 1–6.

In this lesson you will learn about views of solid figures.

Model how to stack blocks as shown in the diagram. Have students stack the blocks and look down at them to get a top view, look at the side of them to get a side view, and look straight at them to get a front view. Have students complete Exercise 1. *How many cubes are in the solid?* 6 *How many cubes do you see when you look down at the solid?* 3 Have students complete Exercises 2–6.

2 Practice Use with Exercises 7–12.

Have students practice identifying views by building their own solid with cubes. Have them try to visualize the top, front, and side views, and then check to see if they were correct.

Error Intervention If students have difficulty drawing the views, have them use the cubes or blocks to recreate each model and view it from each angle.

If You Have More Time Have students use their blocks to create a model, and then draw the front, side, and top views on a separate piece of paper. Then have another student look at the model and draw the front, side, and top views. Check student's work.

3 Assessment

In this lesson students learned about views of solid figures. Use the **Quick Check** problem to assess students' understanding.

Quick Check 🍃 **Formative Assessment**

Display a solid made of cubes. *Draw the top, front, and side views of this solid figure.* Check students' answers.

GEOMETRIC IDEAS

Name _____

Geometric Ideas

Materials crayons, markers, or colored pencils

A **plane** is an endless flat surface, such as this paper if it extended forever.

1. Name another real-world object which could represent a plane. **Sample answer: classroom floor**

Use the diagram at the right to answer 2 to 8.

A **point** is an exact location in space. Check that students color correctly.

2. Draw a circle around point D in orange.

A **line** is a straight path of points that goes on forever in two directions.

3. Trace over line AD in blue.

   Line AD is written $\overleftrightarrow{AD}$.

A **line segment** is a part of a line with two endpoints.

4. Trace over line segment CD in red. Be sure to stop at point C and point D.

   Line segment CD is written $\overline{CD}$.

A **ray** is a part of a line with one endpoint.

5. Trace over ray AB in green. Ray AB is written $\overrightarrow{AB}$.

6. What point is the endpoint in ray AB? **A**

An **angle** is formed by two rays with the same endpoint.

7. Trace over angle ACB in brown. Angle ACB is written ∠ACB.

The common endpoint of the rays is called the **vertex** of the angle.

8. Which point is the vertex of ∠ACB? **C**

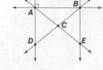

113 (student p. 1) MDIS 2.0

Name _____

Geometric Ideas (continued)

Parallel lines never cross and stay the same distance apart. The symbol ‖ means *is parallel to.*

9. Trace over two lines that appear to be parallel, in purple.

10. Write the names of the parallel lines using the line symbol over the letters.

    $\overleftrightarrow{AD}$ ‖ $\overleftrightarrow{BE}$ Check that students color correctly.

Intersecting lines have a point in common.

11. Trace over two lines that intersect, in yellow.

12. At what point do the lines intersect? **Sample answer: A**

Perpendicular lines intersect and form a right angle. The symbol ⊥ means *is perpendicular to.*

13. Trace over two lines that are perpendicular, in orange.

14. Write the names of the perpendicular lines using the line symbol over the letters. $\overleftrightarrow{AD}$ ⊥ $\overleftrightarrow{AB}$

Draw each of the following.

15. ray HJ   16. line segment KL   17. line RS

18. $\overleftrightarrow{TV}$ is parallel to $\overleftrightarrow{WX}$.   19. $\overline{EF}$ is perpendicular to $\overleftrightarrow{JK}$.   20. $\overleftrightarrow{YZ}$ intersects $\overrightarrow{AB}$.

113 (student p. 2) MDIS 2.0

Objective Students will learn about geometric ideas.

Vocabulary Angle, intersecting lines, line, line segment, parallel lines, perpendicular lines, plane, point, ray

Materials Crayons, markers, or colored pencils

❶ Conceptual Development
Use with Exercises 1–14.

In this lesson you will learn about geometric ideas.

Revisit the terms *angle, intersecting lines, line, line segment, parallel lines, perpendicular lines, plane, point,* and *ray* as needed. Read and complete Exercise 1 together. *What is a plane?* An endless flat surface Read the statement about each of the other geometric terms together, and have students identify each idea on the diagram. *How are points and lines related?* Points make up a line. *How are lines and line segments related?* A line segment is a part of a line. *How are rays and angles related?* An angle is formed by two rays with the same endpoint. *What are parallel lines?* Lines that never cross and stay the same distance apart Have students complete Exercises 2–14.

❷ Practice Use with Exercises 15–20.

Remind students to refer back to the definition of each term before beginning each drawing.

Error Intervention If students have difficulty differentiating between rays and lines, point out that a ray has one endpoint and one arrow, and a line has two arrows.

If You Have More Time Have students draw an example of each term and have a partner identify what they have drawn. Check student's work.

❸ Assessment

In this lesson students learned about geometric ideas. Use the **Quick Check** problem to assess students' understanding.

Quick Check  **Formative Assessment**

Have students draw two intersecting lines and identify an angle, a point, a line, and a line segment. Check students' answers.

Name _____

Congruent Figures

Materials tracing paper and scissors

Two figures that have exactly the same size and shape are congruent.

1. Place a piece of paper over Figure A and trace the shape. Is the figure you drew congruent to Figure A? ___yes___

Cut out the figure you traced and use it to answer 2 to 10.

Figure A

Figure B   **Figure C**   **Figure D**

2. Place the cutout on top of Figure B. Is Figure B the same size as Figure A? ___no___

3. Is Figure B congruent to Figure A? ___no___

4. Place the cutout on top of Figure C. Is Figure C the same shape as Figure A? ___no___

5. Is Figure C congruent to Figure A? ___no___

6. Place the cutout on top of Figure D. Is Figure D the same size as Figure A? ___yes___

7. Is Figure D the same shape as Figure A? ___yes___

8. Is Figure D congruent to Figure A? ___yes___

9. Circle the figure that is congruent to the figure at the right.

114 (student p. 1)   MDIS 2.0

Name _____

Congruent Figures (continued)

Tell if the two figures are congruent. Write Yes or No.

10. ⬡ ⬡ ___yes___   11. △ △ ___no___   12. ◁ ▷ ___yes___

13. ⬠ ⬠ ___yes___   14. ▭ ▭ ___no___   15. ▱ ▱ ___no___

16. ○ ○ ___yes___   17. ⊔ ⊔ ___no___   18. ▫ ▯ ___no___

19. Divide the isosceles triangle shown at the right into 2 congruent right triangles.

20. Divide the hexagon shown at the right into 6 congruent equilateral triangles.

21. Divide the rectangle shown at the right into 2 pairs of congruent triangles.

22. **Reasoning** Are the triangles at the right congruent? Why or why not?
No; the triangles are the same shape, but they are not the same size.

114 (student p. 2)   MDIS 2.0

Objective Students will identify congruent figures.
Vocabulary Congruent
Materials Tracing paper and scissors

1 Conceptual Development
Use with Exercises 1–9.

In this lesson you will learn to identify congruent figures.

Revisit the term *congruent* as needed. Have students read the statement at the top of the page and then follow the steps in Exercise 1. *How do you know that what you have drawn is congruent to Figure A?* It is the same size and shape as Figure A because I traced it. Have students cut out the figure they traced. *How can you find out if another figure is congruent to this figure?* I can place the cutout on top of the figure and see if it is the same size and shape. Have students complete Exercises 2–9.

2 Practice Use with Exercises 10–22.

Remind students that congruent figures are not only the same shape; they also must be the same size.

Error Intervention If students have difficulty dividing the figures in Exercises 19–21, have them draw and cut out a larger version of each figure and fold it to find congruent figures.

If You Have More Time Have students revisit the figures in Exercises 10–18. If the figures in each exercise are congruent, have them draw one that is not. If the figures in each exercise are not congruent, have them draw a figure that is congruent to each. Check students' drawings.

3 Assessment

In this lesson students learned to identify congruent figures. Use the **Quick Check** problem to assess students' understanding.

Quick Check **Formative** Assessment

Draw two congruent figures and two figures that are not congruent. Tell why the two figures are congruent and why the other two are not. Check students' work.

CIRCLES

Name _____

Circles

Materials crayons, markers, or colored pencils

Use the figure at the right to answer 1 to 10.

A **circle** is the set of all points in a plane that are the same distance from a point called the **center**.

1. Color the point that is the center of the circle red.

A **radius** is any line that connects the center of the circle to a point on the circle.

2. Color a radius of the circle blue.

3. **Reasoning** Will every radius that is drawn on the circle have same length? Explain your answer.
   Yes; every point on the circle is the same distance from the center.

A **chord** is a line segment that connects any two points on a circle. A chord may or may not go through the center of the circle.

4. Color a chord on the circle that does not include the center of the circle, green.

5. **Reasoning** Will every chord that is drawn on the circle have the same length? Explain your answer.
   No; chords can be different lengths because they do not have to pass through the center of the circle.

A **diameter** is a chord that goes through the center of the circle.

6. Color a diameter of the circle orange.

7. **Reasoning** Will every diameter that is drawn on the circle have the same length? Explain your answer.
   Yes; a diameter is two radii and all radii are the same length. So, diameters of a circle are the same length.

Check that students color correctly.

Name _____

Circles (continued)

The length of the diameter of a circle is two times the length of the radius.

8. Use a centimeter ruler to measure the length of the radius. What is the length of the radius?   __3__ cm

9. Use a centimeter ruler to measure the length of the diameter. What is the length of the diameter?   __6__ cm

10. Is the diameter two times the length of the radius?   __yes__

Identify the part of each circle indicated by the arrow.

11. _____ center

12. _____ radius

13. _____ chord

14. _____ center

15. _____ diameter

16. _____ chord

Find the radius or diameter of each circle.

17. (6 in.) radius: ___3 in.___

18. (5 ft) diameter: ___10 ft___

19. (18 cm) radius: ___9 cm___

20. The radius of a circle is 11 centimeters. What is the diameter of the circle?   ___22 cm___

Objective Students will learn about circles.
Vocabulary Circle, center, chord, diameter, radius
Materials Centimeter ruler, crayons, markers, or colored pencils

① Conceptual Development
Use with Exercises 1–10.

In this lesson you will learn about circles.

Revisit the terms *circle, center, chord, diameter,* and *radius* as needed. Read the statement at the top of the page together. Have students complete Exercise 1 by coloring the center of the circle red. Have students read the statements and directives in Exercises 2–10. Discuss each part of the circle as it is identified. *How are the center of the circle and the radius related?* A radius goes from the center of the circle to a point on the circle. *How are the radius and diameter related?* The radius is half of the diameter. *How is a chord formed?* Draw a line from one point on the circle to another point on the circle Have students complete Exercises 2–10.

② Practice Use with Exercises 11–20.

Have students refer to the colored circle they just completed to help them identify each part of a circle.

Error Intervention If students have difficulty identifying the parts of a circle, have them recreate the circle diagram on a larger sheet of paper, labeling each part of the circle by writing the word and drawing an arrow to the part it refers to.

If You Have More Time Have students draw another radius on the circle in Exercise 17. *What is the length of the radius you drew?* 3 inches *How do you know?* All radii in a circle have the same measure.

③ Assessment

In this lesson students learned about circles. Use the **Quick Check** problem to assess students' understanding.

Quick Check **Formative** Assessment

Tell the difference between a radius and a chord, and a radius and a diameter. If you know the radius of a circle, how can you find the diameter? If you know the diameter, how can you find the radius? Check students' answers.

ROTATIONAL SYMMETRY

Name _____

Rotational Symmetry

Materials paper and scissors

If a figure can be turned less than a full turn about a point and fit back on itself, then the figure has **rotational symmetry**.

All turns in this activity are assumed to be clockwise. Find the types of rotational symmetry for the figure shown at the right by answering 1 to 11.

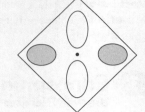

1. Place a piece of paper over the figure shown and trace it. Cut out the figure.

2. Place the cutout on top of the original figure, put your pencil on the dots to hold them in place, and rotate 90 degrees clockwise or to the right around the point.

3. Does the cutout fit on top of the original figure? _____ no

4. Does the figure have 90° rotational symmetry? _____ no

5. Rotate the figure an additional 90 degrees clockwise around the point for a total of 180 degrees.

6. Does the cutout fit on top of the original figure? _____ yes

7. Does the figure have 180° rotational symmetry? _____ yes

8. Rotate the shape an additional 90 degrees clockwise around the point for a total of 270 degrees.

9. Does the cutout fit on top of the original figure? _____ no

10. Does the figure have 270° rotational symmetry? _____ no

11. What types of rotational symmetry does the figure have? _____ 180°

116 (student p. 1)   MDIS 2.0

Name _____

Rotational Symmetry (continued)

Write 90°, 180°, 270°, or none to describe the rotational symmetry of each figure.

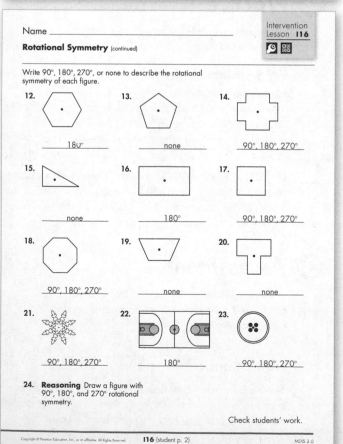

12. _____ 180°

13. _____ none

14. _____ 90°, 180°, 270°

15. _____ none

16. _____ 180°

17. _____ 90°, 180°, 270°

18. _____ 90°, 180°, 270°

19. _____ none

20. _____ none

21. _____ 90°, 180°, 270°

22. _____ 180°

23. _____ 90°, 180°, 270°

24. **Reasoning** Draw a figure with 90°, 180°, and 270° rotational symmetry.

Check students' work.

116 (student p. 2)   MDIS 2.0

Objective Students will learn about rotational symmetry.

Vocabulary Rotational symmetry

Materials Paper and scissors

① Conceptual Development
Use with Exercises 1–11.

In this lesson you will learn about rotational symmetry.

Revisit the term *rotational symmetry* as needed. Have students read the paragraphs at the top of the page and cut out the figure by completing Exercise 1. *How is rotational symmetry different from line symmetry?* Sample answer: A figure has rotational symmetry if you can turn the figure and place it exactly on itself. A figure has line symmetry if you can fold the figure in half over a line and the two halves of the figure match. *Can a shape have both rotational and line symmetry? Explain.* Yes; Sample answer: A rectangle has 180 degree rotational symmetry, and it has line symmetry when a line is draw horizontally or vertically through its center. Have students complete Exercises 2–11.

② Practice Use with Exercises 12–24.

Remind students that after the turn has been made, the figure must fit directly on top of the other to have rotational symmetry.

Error Intervention If students have difficulty determining rotational symmetry, have them cut out a figure and rotate it to determine rotational symmetry.

If You Have More Time Have students find the uppercase letters of the alphabet that have rotational symmetry. H, I, N, O, S, X, and Z

③ Assessment

In this lesson students learned about rotational symmetry. Use the **Quick Check** problem to assess students' understanding.

Quick Check   **Formative** Assessment

Write in words the steps needed to determine whether a shape has rotational symmetry. Check student's explanations.

TRANSFORMATIONS

Materials paper, scissors, and markers.

Transformations do not change the size or shape of a figure. There are three types of transformations: translation, reflection, and rotation.

Use a piece of paper to trace the house figure shown on the grid. Then, cut it out. Answer 1 to 8.

A **translation** is a slide.

1. Place the cutout shape over the shape on the grid. What are the coordinates of each of the 5 vertices of the pentagon?

   (1, 6), (1, 9), (3, 11), (5, 9), (5, 6)

2. Slide the cutout shape 5 units to the right and trace around it. What are the coordinates of each of the 5 vertices after the translation?

   (6, 6), (6, 9), (8, 11), (10, 9), (10, 6)

3. Now slide the cutout shape 6 units down so that it is 5 units to the right and 6 units down from the original position and trace around it. What are the coordinates of each vertex after the translation?

   (6, 0), (6, 3), (8, 5), (10, 3), (10, 0)

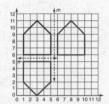

A **reflection** is a flip or a mirror image.

4. Place the cutout shape over the shape shown on the grid. Flip the house over line *m* and trace around it. The left side of the shape in the new position should be the same distance from the line as the right side was in the original position.

5. Place the cutout shape back in the original position. Flip the house over line *n* and trace around it.

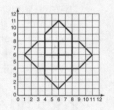

117 (student p. 1)　　　　MDIS 2.0

A **rotation** is a turn that moves a figure about a point. Each quarter turn is the same as a 90 degree rotation.

6. Place the cutout shape over the shape on the grid. Make a mark on the cutout at the same place as the dot. Turn the shape around the point clockwise so that the roof on the house is now pointing to the right or at 3 o'clock. The mark on the cutout should still be touching the point. Trace around the figure. This is a $\frac{1}{4}$ turn. How many degrees did the figure rotate?

   90 degrees

7. Rotate the shape a total of 180 degrees, or $\frac{1}{2}$ turn, from the original and trace around it. In what direction is the roof of the house now pointing?

   down or 6 o'clock

8. Rotate the shape a total of 270 degrees, or $\frac{3}{4}$ turn, from the original and trace around it. In what direction is the roof pointing?

   left or 9 o'clock

Tell whether the figures in each pair are related by a translation, a reflection, or a rotation.

9.
reflection

10.
rotation

11.
translation

12.
translation

13.
reflection

14.
rotation

117 (student p. 2)　　　　MDIS 2.0

Objective Students will learn about transformations.
Vocabulary Reflection, rotation, transformation, translation
Materials Paper, scissors, and markers

① Conceptual Development
Use with Exercises 1–8.

In this lesson you will learn about transformations.

Revisit the terms *reflection, rotation, translation,* and *transformation* as needed. Have students read the paragraphs at the top of the page, cut out the figure as directed, and complete Exercise 1. *What are the coordinates of the top vertex of the pentagon?* (3, 11). *Would a transformation change the shape of this figure? Explain.* No; Sample answer: When a shape is reflected, rotated, or translated, it does not change the shape of the figure, only the position and orientation of the figure. Have students complete Exercises 2–8.

② Practice Use with Exercises 9–14.

To identify each transformation, encourage students to explain in words how they would use a cutout to move from one figure to the other.

Error Intervention If students have difficulty differentiating the types of transformations, have them create note cards, each with the name, a description, and an example of one transformation.

If You Have More Time Have students use grid paper to make their own example of a translation, a reflection, and a rotation, and have them label each. Check students' work.

③ Assessment

In this lesson students learned about transformations. Use the **Quick Check** problem to assess students' understanding.

Quick Check **Formative** Assessment

Write or tell how you know that the figures in Exercises 9 are related by a reflection. The figures are mirror images of each other.

Student Page 1

Name _____

Measuring and Classifying Angles

Materials protractor, straightedge, and crayons, markers, or colored pencils

A protractor can be used to measure and draw angles. Angles are measured in degrees.

Use a protractor to measure the angle shown by answering 1 to 2.

1. Place the protractor's center on the angle's vertex and place the 0° mark on one side of the angle.

2. Read the measure where the other side of the angle crosses the protractor. What is the measure of the angle? _____ 100°

Use a protractor to draw an angle with a measure of 60° by answering 3 to 5.

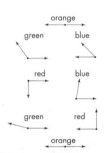

3. Draw $\overrightarrow{AB}$ by connecting the points shown with the endpoint of the ray at point A.

4. Place the protractor's center on point A. Place the protractor so the the 0° mark is lined up with $\overrightarrow{AB}$.

5. Place a point at 60°. Label it C and draw $\overrightarrow{AC}$.

Use a protractor to measure the angles shown, if necessary, to answer 6 to 9.

6. **Acute** angles have a measure between 0° and 90°. Trace over the acute angles with blue.

7. **Right** angles have a measure of 90°. Trace over the right angles with red.

8. **Obtuse** angles have a measure between 90° and 180°. Trace over the obtuse angles with green.

9. **Straight** angles have a measure of 180°. Trace over the straight angles with orange.

orange

green   blue

red   blue

green   red

orange

118 (student p. 1)   MDIS 2.0

Student Page 2

Name _____

Measuring and Classifying Angles (continued)

Classify each angle as acute, right, obtuse, or straight. Then measure the angle.

10.
acute;
_____ 30°

11.
acute;
_____ 75°

12.
obtuse;
_____ 115°

13.
obtuse;
_____ 160°

14.
acute;
_____ 15°

15.
acute;
_____ 45°

Use a protractor to draw an angle with each measure.

16. 120°   17. 35°   18. 70°

19. **Reasoning** If two acute angles are placed next to each other to form one angle, will the result always be an obtuse angle? Explain. Provide a drawing in your explanation.
No; both acute angles could be small enough so that the sum of their measures is less than 90° or equal to 90°. Check student's drawings.

118 (student p. 2)   MDIS 2.0

Objective Students will measure and classify angles.
Vocabulary Angle, acute angle, right angle, obtuse angle, straight angle, protractor
Materials Protractor, straightedge, and crayons, markers, or colored pencils

1 Conceptual Development
Use with Exercises 1–9.

In this lesson you will learn to measure and classify angles.

Revisit the terms *angle, acute angle, right angle, obtuse angle, straight angle*, and *protractor* as needed. Have students read aloud the statements at the top of the page and direct them to the angle to the right. *How can we tell that this is an angle?* It shows 2 rays with a common vertex. Have students follow the steps described in Exercises 1–2 to measure the angle. *What is the measure of the angle?* 100 degrees *Is this angle greater than or less than a right angle?* Greater than Have students complete Exercises 3–9.

2 Practice Use with Exercises 10–19.

Encourage students to classify the angles first and then measure them.

Error Intervention If students have difficulty drawing angles, have them draw two points and join them using a straightedge. Then show how to put the protractor's center on the leftmost point, find the angle measure, mark it with a point, and then draw a line segment to complete the angle.

If You Have More Time Have partners name an angle measure (e.g., 115°) and have each draw the angle and classify it. Then have them compare their drawings and answers. Check students' work.

3 Assessment

In this lesson students learned to measure and classify angles. Use the **Quick Check** problem to assess students' understanding.

Quick Check **Formative Assessment**

Draw an example of an acute angle and an obtuse angle and write each measure. Check students' work.

118   MDIS 2.0

ANGLE PAIRS

Name _____

Angle Pairs

Adjacent angles are a pair of angles with a common vertex and a common side but no common interior points.

1. The picture at the right shows adjacent angles. Trace over the common side in the picture.

2. Name the two adjacent angles that share the side you traced.

   ∠ADB and ∠BDC

Complementary angles are two angles whose measures add up to 90 degrees. **Supplementary angles** are two angles whose measures add up to 180 degrees.

3. One of the right angles in the diagram is formed by two smaller angles. These two angles are complementary. Name the complementary angles.

   ∠SET and ∠TEV

4. What is the measure of ∠SET? 55°

5. What is the measure of ∠TEV? 35°

6. Name an angle in the picture whose measure is 180°. ∠REV

7. Angle REV is divided into two angles, ∠RET and another one. Draw an arc on ∠RET. Name the other angle that makes up ∠REV. These two angles are supplementary. ∠TEV

8. What angle is supplementary to ∠RES? ∠SEV

When two lines intersect, angles are formed. Angles that are opposite one another with no common side are called **vertical angles**. Vertical angles have the same measure.

119 (student p. 1) MDIS 2.0

Name _____

Angle Pairs (continued)

9. Draw an arc on ∠WOX. Name an angle in the picture that does not have a common side with ∠WOX.

   ∠YOZ

10. What type of angles are ∠WOX and ∠YOZ? Write the measure of ∠WOX on the picture. vertical

11. What type of angles are ∠WOY and ∠YOZ? Write the measure of ∠WOY on the picture. supplementary

12. What types of angles are ∠WOY and ∠XOZ? vertical

Find the measure of each angle labeled with a letter.

13.  151°

14.   165°

15. 57°

16.   45°

Find the measure of an angle that is complementary to an angle with each measure.

17. 84° 6°

18. 4° 86°

19. 16° 74°

20. 72° 18°

Find the measure of each angle by using the picture at the right.

21. ∠NOT 22°

22. ∠PON 68°

23. ∠POQ 90°

24. ∠ROS 117°

25. **Reasoning** What word can be used to describe two intersecting lines whose vertical angles are 90°? perpendicular

119 (student p. 2) MDIS 2.0

🕐

Objective Students will identify angle pairs.
Vocabulary Adjacent angles, complementary angles, supplementary angles, vertical angles

1 Conceptual Development
Use with Exercises 1–12.

In this lesson you will learn to identify angle pairs.

Have students read the definition at the top of the page. *Adjacent angles* are one type of angle pair. *What do they have in common?* A common vertex and a common side *What do they not have in common?* Interior points Have students complete Exercises 1–2. Introduce *complementary angles* and *supplementary angles*. *What is the sum of the measures of complementary angles?* 90° *What is the sum of the measures of supplementary angles?* 180° Define *vertical angles*. *What do you know about vertical angles?* Their measures are equal. Have students complete Exercises 3–12.

2 Practice Use with Exercises 13–25.

Explain that right angles are always marked with a right-angle box. Tell students that without the box, even if the angle looks like a right angle, they cannot assume that it is a right angle.

Error Intervention If students have difficulty finding vertical angles, have them highlight the two sides of the angles to see whether they form straight lines.

If You Have More Time Have students make their own angle puzzle involving missing angle measures and using adjacent, complementary, vertical, or supplementary angles. Have them trade with a partner and solve each other's puzzles. Check students' work.

3 Assessment

In this lesson students learned to identify angle pairs. Use the **Quick Check** problem to assess students' understanding.

Quick Check **Formative** Assessment

Draw a pair of angles that are supplementary but not adjacent. Check students' work.

Name _____

Intervention
Lesson 120

Missing Angles in Triangles and Quadrilaterals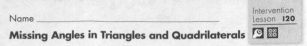

Materials index card and scissors

Find the relationship among angles in a triangle by answering 1 to 9.

1. Draw a triangle on an index card and cut it out.

2. Label each angle in the triangle with A, B, and C.

3. Cut out each corner of your triangle so that angles A, B, and C are separated from the triangle.   ◄-------•

4. Start with angle A. Place the vertex on the point shown above and one side of the angle on the dashed line. Trace around the angle.

5. Next place angle B's vertex on the point and one side of the angle so that it is sharing a side with angle A. Trace around the angle.

6. Next place angle C's vertex on the point and one side of the angle so that it is sharing a side with angle B. Trace around the angle.

7. **Reasoning** What do you notice about the angles of a triangle?

   They form a straight line or 180 degrees.

8. Compare your results with that of other students. Do the angles of the triangle have the same relationship?   _____yes_____

9. What is the sum of the measures of the three angles in any triangle?   _____180°_____

Find the relationship among angles in a quadrilateral by answering 10 to 16.

10. Draw a quadrilateral, that does not have any right angles, on an index card and cut it out.

11. Label each of the angles in the quadrilateral with A, B, C, and D.

Name _____

Intervention
Lesson 120

Missing Angles in Triangles and Quadrilaterals (continued)

12. Cut out each corner of your quadrilateral so that angles A, B, C, and D are separated from the quadrilateral.   ◄-------•

13. Place the vertex of each angle on the point shown. Position the angles so that they are adjacent and share a common side.

14. **Reasoning** What do you notice about the angles of a quadrilateral?

   They form a circle or 360 degrees.

15. Compare your results with that of other students. Do the angles of their quadrilateral have the same relationship?   _____yes_____

16. What is the sum of the measures of the four angles in a quadrilateral?   _____360°_____

Find the missing angle measures.

17.
   55°

18.
   125°

19.
   63°

20.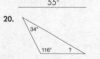
   30°

21.
   65°

22.
   19°

Objective Students will find missing angles in triangles and quadrilaterals.
Vocabulary Triangle, quadrilateral
Materials Index card, scissors

❶ Conceptual Development
Use with Exercises 1–16.

In this lesson you will learn to find missing angles in triangles and quadrilaterals.

Review the definition of a *triangle. How many angles does a triangle have?* 3 Ask students to draw a triangle on their index cards. *How many degrees are in a straight line?* 180° Tell students that they will be finding the sum of the angles of a triangle. Have students complete Exercises 1–9. *What is the sum of the measures of the 3 angles in a triangle?* 180° *How do you find the missing angle in a triangle when you know two angles?* Add the two measures that you know and subtract the sum from 180 Review the definition of a *quadrilateral. How many angles does a quadrilateral have?* 4 Have students complete Exercises 10–16.

❷ Practice Use with Exercises 17–22.

Remind students that the sum of the angles in any triangle is 180° and that the type of triangle does not change this fact. Likewise, remind them that the sum of the angles in any quadrilateral is 360°.

Error Intervention If students have difficulty remembering the sum of the angles in a quadrilateral, show them how to divide a quadrilateral into two triangles by drawing a diagonal. Show that the sum of the angles will be 2 × 180°.

If You Have More Time Have students draw their own quadrilateral and measure the angles to find the sum of the angles. Check students' work.

❸ Assessment

In this lesson students learned to find missing angles in triangles and quadrilaterals. Use the **Quick Check** problem to assess students' understanding.

Quick Check **Formative** Assessment

A right triangle has one angle that measures 36°. What is the measure of the other angle that is not the right angle? 54°

Name _____

Measuring Length to $\frac{1}{2}$ and $\frac{1}{4}$ Inch

Intervention
Lesson **121**

Materials inch ruler for each student, crayons or markers.

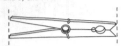

The distance between 0 and 1 on the ruler is one inch. So is the space between 1 and 2, 2 and 3, and so on.

1. Line up the left edge of the clothespin with the 0 mark on the ruler. Is the clothespin's length closer to the 2 inch mark or the 3 inch mark? _____ 3 inch mark

2. What is the clothespin's length to the nearest inch? _____ 3 inches

3. How many spaces are between 0 and 1 on the ruler above? _____ 4

4. So each space is what part of an inch? _____ $\frac{1}{4}$

5. Color the marks in the ruler above that are $\frac{1}{4}$ inch and $\frac{3}{4}$ inch from zero red. Then color the rest of the $\frac{1}{4}$ inch marks red including $1\frac{1}{4}$, $1\frac{3}{4}$, $2\frac{1}{4}$, $2\frac{3}{4}$, and so on. Color the mark that is $\frac{2}{4}$ or $\frac{1}{2}$ inch from zero blue. Then color the rest of the $\frac{1}{2}$ inch marks blue, including $1\frac{1}{2}$, $2\frac{1}{2}$, and so on.

6. What is the length of the clothespin to the nearest $\frac{1}{2}$ inch? _____ $2\frac{1}{2}$ inches

Measure the length of the cricket to the nearest inch, $\frac{1}{2}$ inch and $\frac{1}{4}$ inch.

7. nearest inch _____ 1 _____ inch

8. nearest $\frac{1}{2}$ inch _____ $1\frac{1}{2}$ _____ inches   9. nearest $\frac{1}{4}$ inch _____ $1\frac{1}{4}$ _____ inches

121 (student p. 1)   MDIS 2.0

Name _____

Measuring Length to $\frac{1}{2}$ and $\frac{1}{4}$ Inch (continued)

Intervention
Lesson **121**

Measure each object to the nearest inch, $\frac{1}{2}$ inch, and $\frac{1}{4}$ inch.

10. Nearest inch: _____ 3 _____ inches

11. Nearest $\frac{1}{2}$ inch: _____ 3 _____ inches

    Nearest $\frac{1}{4}$ inch: _____ $2\frac{3}{4}$ _____ inches

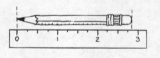

12. Nearest inch: _____ 3 _____ inches

13. Nearest $\frac{1}{2}$ inch: _____ $2\frac{1}{2}$ _____ inches

    Nearest $\frac{1}{4}$ inch: _____ $2\frac{3}{4}$ _____ inches

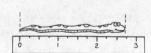

14. Nearest inch: _____ 1 _____ inch

15. Nearest $\frac{1}{2}$ inch: _____ $1\frac{1}{2}$ _____ inches

    Nearest $\frac{1}{4}$ inch: _____ $1\frac{1}{4}$ _____ inches

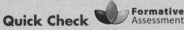

16. **Reasoning** Which gives the closest measurement, measuring to the nearest inch, $\frac{1}{2}$ inch, or $\frac{1}{4}$ inch? Explain.

    Sample answer: Measuring to the nearest $\frac{1}{4}$ inch gives the closest measurement because there are more $\frac{1}{4}$ marks than $\frac{1}{2}$ inch or inch marks.

121 (student p. 2)   MDIS 2.0

Objective Students will measure lengths to $\frac{1}{2}$ and $\frac{1}{4}$ inch.
Vocabulary Ruler, inch
Materials Inch ruler for each student, crayons or markers

① Conceptual Development
Use with Exercises 1–9.

In this lesson you will learn to measure lengths to $\frac{1}{2}$ and $\frac{1}{4}$ inch.

Remind students how to use a *ruler*. *What can you use a ruler to measure?* Length Ask students to identify how long an *inch* is. *How long is an inch on the ruler?* It is the distance between two numbers. *How many inches are on your ruler?* Answers may vary, but most likely there will be 12. *Where on the ruler do you line up an object to measure its length?* At the 0 mark *How long is the clothespin to the nearest inch?* 3 inches Have students complete Exercises 1–2. *How many equal parts is each inch divided into on the ruler on the page?* 4 *What part of an inch is each space?* $\frac{1}{4}$ inch *What fraction is $\frac{2}{4}$ equivalent to?* $\frac{1}{2}$ Have students complete Exercises 3–9.

② Practice Use with Exercises 10–16.

Review fractions on a number line. Relate the fractions on a number line to a ruler. Show how the tick marks divide the spaces or the inches into equal parts.

Error Intervention If students have difficulty understanding what each tick mark on the ruler means, have them use a paper ruler and write the fraction for each tick mark on it.

If You Have More Time Have students choose three objects in the classroom and measure them to the nearest $\frac{1}{2}$ inch and to the nearest $\frac{1}{4}$ inch. Ask if any of the objects had the same measurement when measured to the $\frac{1}{2}$ inch and to the $\frac{1}{4}$ inch. Check students' work.

③ Assessment

In this lesson students learned to measure lengths to $\frac{1}{2}$ and $\frac{1}{4}$ inch. Use the **Quick Check** problem to assess students' understanding.

Quick Check 🌷 **Formative Assessment**

Measure a new unsharpened pencil to the nearest $\frac{1}{2}$ inch. Sample answer: $7\frac{1}{2}$ inches

Name _____

Using Customary Units of Length

A small paperclip is about 1 *inch* long.

A football is about 1 *foot* long.

A baseball bat is about 1 *yard* long.

Most people can walk a *mile* in about 15 minutes.

What is the best unit to measure each?

1. The length of your pencil _____inches_____

2. The length of the Mississippi River _____miles_____

3. The height of a desk _____feet_____

4. The length of your school _____yards_____

Answer 5 to 7 and use the table to find how many inches are in 4 feet.

5. 1 foot = _12_ inches

6. To find how many inches are in 4 feet, multiply 4 × 12 inches.

   4 × 12 inches = _48_ inches

7. How many inches are in 4 feet? _48_

Answer 8 to 10 and use the table to find how many feet are in 5 yards, 2 feet.

8. 1 yard = _3_ feet

9. How many feet are in 5 yards?   5 × 3 feet = _15_ feet

10. How many feet are in 3 yards, 2 feet?   15 feet + 2 feet = _17_ feet

Customary Units of Length	
1 foot (ft) = 12 inches	
1 yard (yd) = 3 feet	
1 yard = 36 inches	
1 mile (mi) = 5,280 feet	
1 mile = 1,760 yards	

122 (student p. 1)   MDIS 2.0

Name _____

Using Customary Units of Length (continued)

Which unit would you use to measure each item? Write *inch*, *foot*, *yard*, or *mile*.

11. The length of a gerbil
    _____inch_____

12. The length of a football field
    _____yard_____

13. The height of a door
    _____foot_____

14. The distance to the sun
    _____mile_____

Circle the better estimate.

15. The distance you travel on an airplane

    560 yards or (560 miles)

16. The height of a full grown adult giraffe

    6 feet or (6 yards)

17. The length of a bar of soap

    (3 inches) or 7 inches

18. The length of your bed

    (7 feet) or 7 yards

Find each missing number.

19. 2 yards = _6_ feet

20. 3 feet = _36_ inches

21. 4 yards = _144_ inches

22. 3 yards, 2 feet = _11_ feet

23. 1 foot, 9 inches = _21_ inches

24. 2 yards, 2 feet = _96_ inches

25. **Reasoning** What unit would you use to measure the length of an earthworm? Explain why your choice is the best unit.

    Inches; An earthworm is less than a foot long, so any unit other than inches would be too large.

122 (student p. 2)   MDIS 2.0

Objective Students will use customary units of length.

Vocabulary Inch, foot, yard, mile, customary

① Conceptual Development
Use with Exercises 1–10.

In this lesson you will learn to use customary units of length.

Provide objects or images of common objects that represent an approximate *inch, foot, yard,* and *mile*. Identify each of these as *customary* units of length. *What else is about an inch long?* Answers will vary. Repeat with the other units. Have students complete Exercises 1–4. Explain that there are relationships among the different units. *How many inches are in a foot?* 12 *How many feet are in a yard?* 3 *So how many inches are in a yard?* 36 *What are two measurements that are equal to a mile?* 5,280 feet and 1,760 yards Have students complete Exercises 5–7. Explain that sometimes more than one unit is used to measure length. Ask for a few volunteers to tell their height, which is usually given in feet and inches. Have students complete Exercises 8–10.

② Practice **Use with Exercises 11–25.**

Point out to students that the same distance will require more of the smaller units of measure.

Error Intervention If students have difficulty estimating length, encourage them to use the examples given at the top of the first page.

If You Have More Time Have students go on a scavenger hunt to find objects of a given length. Make sure all of the lengths are in customary units. Check students' work.

③ Assessment

In this lesson students learned to use customary units of length. Use the **Quick Check** problem to assess students' understanding.

Quick Check   **Formative Assessment**

How many inches are there in 2 yards 14 inches? 86 inches

USING METRIC UNITS OF LENGTH

Name _____

Using Metric Units of Length

Materials centimeter ruler for each student

Your finger is about 1 centimeter wide.

1. Use the width of your finger to estimate the length of the pencil.
   Answers will vary.
   Estimate: _____ of my finger widths = about _____ centimeters

2. Line up the 0 mark on the ruler with the left edge of the pencil.

3. What is the length of the pencil
   to the nearest centimeter?   ____11____ centimeters

A dime is about 1 *millimeter* thick.

A new crayon is almost
1 *decimeter* long.

A door knob is about 1 *meter*
above the floor.

Most people can walk a
kilometer in about 10 minutes.

1 meter

What is the best unit to measure each?

4. the length of your finger   centimeters

5. the distance across your state   kilometers

6. the length of a lady bug   millimeters

123 (student p. 1)   MDIS 2.0

Name _____

Using Metric Units of Length (continued)

Answer 7 to 9 and use the table to find how many centimeters
are in 4 meters, 76 centimeters.

7. 1 meter = ___100___ centimeters

8. How many centimeters are
   in 4 meters?
   4 × 100 cm = ·400 cm

Metric Units of Length		
1 centimeter (cm)	=	10 millimeters
1 decimeter (dm)	=	10 centimeters
1 meter (m)	=	100 centimeters
1 kilometer (km)	=	1,000 meters

9. How many centimeters are in
   4 meters, 76 centimeters?
   400 cm + 76 cm = ___476___ cm

Estimate the length of the spoon. Then measure to the
nearest centimeter.

10.
   ____13 centimeters____

What unit would you use to measure each item?
Write *millimeter, centimeter, decimeter, meter,* or *kilometer.*

11. An adult's height   12. Distance traveled on vacation
    _____meter_____   _____kilometer_____

Choose the best estimate.

13. Length of a car   14. Length of a calculator
    5 decimeters or (5 meters)   (12 centimeters) or 12 decimeters

Find each missing number.

15. 3 meters 18 centimeters = ___318___ centimeters

16. 6 meters 3 centimeters = ___603___ centimeters

123 (student p. 2)   MDIS 2.0

Objective Students will use metric units of length.
Vocabulary Centimeter, millimeter, decimeter, meter, kilometer, metric
Materials Centimeter ruler for each student

1 Conceptual Development
Use with Exercises 1–9.

In this lesson you will learn to use metric units of length.

Explain that the width of a finger is about 1 *centimeter*. *How can you use your finger to estimate the length of an object in centimeters?* Determine how many finger widths long the object is *How could you check your estimate of the object's length?* Measure the object with a ruler Discuss using a ruler to measure to the nearest centimeter. Have students complete Exercises 1–3. Discuss everyday objects that represent an approximate *millimeter, decimeter, meter,* and *kilometer.* Identify all of these as *metric* units of length. Explain that there are relationships among the different units. Have students look at the *Metric Units of Length* table. *How many millimeters are in a centimeter?* 10 *How many centimeters are in a meter?* 100 Have students complete Exercises 4–9.

2 Practice Use with Exercises 10–16.

Review patterns of multiplying by powers of 10. Discuss how multiplying moves the decimal point to the right.

Error Intervention If students have difficulty measuring lengths with a ruler, remind them to line up the end of the object with the 0 mark on the ruler. The 0 mark is not necessarily at the end of the ruler.

If You Have More Time Have students go on a scavenger hunt to find objects of a given length. Then have them measure using their centimeter ruler to check their estimates. Check students' work.

3 Assessment

In this lesson students learned to use metric units of length. Use the **Quick Check** problem to assess students' understanding.

Quick Check **Formative** Assessment

How many centimeters are in 4 meters 29 centimeters?
429 centimeters

UNITS OF MEASURE AND PRECISION

Units of Measure and Precision

Name _____

Materials inch and centimeter rulers, rectangle measuring $3\frac{5}{16}$ inches by $\frac{7}{8}$ inches for each student, pair, or group

The smaller the units on the scale of a measuring device, the more precise the measurement.

Explore precision by answering 1 to 12.

1. What are the dimensions of the cut out rectangle to the nearest inch? **3 in. by 1 in.**

2. Draw a rectangle with the dimensions found in item 1. Check students' drawings.

3. What are the dimensions of the cut out rectangle to the nearest eighth inch? **$3\frac{3}{8}$ in. by $\frac{7}{8}$ in.**

4. Draw a rectangle with the dimensions found in item 3. Check students' drawings.

5. Which of the rectangles you drew is closest in size to the cut out rectangle? **$3\frac{3}{8}$ in. by $\frac{7}{8}$ in.**

6. Which unit is more precise, inch or eighth inch? **eighth inch**

7. What are the dimensions of the cut out rectangle to the nearest centimeter? **8 cm by 2 cm**

8. Draw a rectangle with the dimensions found in item 7. Check students' drawings.

9. What are the dimensions of the cut out rectangle to the nearest millimeter? **85 mm by 25 mm**

10. Draw a rectangle with the dimensions found in item 9. Check students' drawings.

137 (student p. 1)   MDIS 2.0

Name _____

Units of Measure and Precision (continued)

11. Which of the last two rectangles you drew is closest in size to the cut out rectangle? **85 mm by 25 mm**

12. Which unit is more precise, centimeter or millimeter? **millimeter**

13. **Reasoning** Which unit is more precise, eighth inch or millimeter? **millimeter**

Find the length of the crayon to each unit.

14. whole inch **2** 15. quarter inch **$2\frac{1}{4}$** 16. eighth inch **$2\frac{1}{8}$**

17. sixteenth inch **$2\frac{2}{16}$** 18. centimeter **5 or 6** 19. millimeter **55**

20. Which measure of the crayon is the most precise? **55 mm**

Measure each line segment to the nearest $\frac{1}{8}$ inch and nearest centimeter.

21. _____   22. _____
   $2\frac{1}{4}$ in.; 5 cm $\frac{3}{4}$ in.; 2 cm

Measure each line segment to the nearest $\frac{1}{16}$ inch and nearest millimeter.

23. _____   24. _____
   $2\frac{5}{16}$ in.; 59 mm $2\frac{12}{16}$ in.; 70 mm

Circle the more precise measure in each.

25. (4 km) or 2 mi   26. 2 gal or (8 L)   27. 3 in. or (4 cm)

137 (student p. 2)   MDIS 2.0

Objective Students will use units of measure to find precision.
Vocabulary Precision
Materials Inch and centimeter rulers, rectangle measuring $3\frac{5}{16}$ inches by $\frac{7}{8}$ inches for each student, pair, or group

1 Conceptual Development
Use with Exercises 1–13.

In this lesson you will learn to use units of measure to find precision.

Explain that the *precision* of a measurement can be improved by using smaller units on the measurement scale. Have students complete Exercise 1–2. *How close was your rectangle to the size of the original rectangle?* Not very close *Why are the measurements off even though you used a ruler?* The dimensions of the rectangle are not in whole inches. *How could you more precisely duplicate the rectangle?* Measure to a unit that is smaller than an inch. Have students complete Exercises 3–6. *Which do you predict will be more precise: centimeters or millimeters?* Millimeters Have students complete Exercises 7–13.

2 Practice Use with Exercises 14–27.

Remind students how to use a ruler. Tell them to be sure to line up the left end of the object they are measuring with the 0 mark on the ruler.

Error Intervention If students have difficulty determining which measurement is more precise, ask them which would be more precise, measuring their height using yards or inches. Inches would be more precise because it is the smaller unit of measure.

If You Have More Time Have students measure the face of a rectangular box, such as a cereal box. Then have them make a poster showing the size of the face measured with different precisions. Check students' work.

3 Assessment

In this lesson students learned to use units of measure to find precision. Use the **Quick Check** problem to assess students' understanding.

Quick Check 🪷 **Formative Assessment**

Which is more precise: 3 inches or 12 millimeters?
12 millimeters

Name _____

Intervention
Lesson **138**

More Units of Time

Natalia, one of the finalists at a dance marathon, danced 1,740 minutes. Tony, the other finalist, danced 28 hours and 20 minutes. Which finalist danced the longest?

Solve by answering 1 to 6.

To change a smaller unit to a larger unit, divide. To change a larger unit to a smaller unit, multiply.

Units of Time
1 minute = 60 seconds
1 hour = 60 minutes
1 day = 24 hours
1 week = 7 days
1 month = about 4 weeks
1 year = 52 weeks
1 year = 12 months
1 year = 365 days
1 leap year = 366 days
1 decade = 10 years
1 century = 100 years
1 millennium = 1,000 years

1. How many minutes are in an hour?   __60__

2. Do you need to multiply or divide to change from minutes to hours?   __divide__

3. What is 1,740 ÷ 60?   __29__

4. How many hours equal 1,740 minutes?   __29__

5. Compare. Write >, <, or =.

   1,740 min $>$ 28 h 20 min

6. Which finalist danced the longest?   __Natalia__

Fred is two years and ten days older than Ron. Alfonzo is 745 days older than Ron. Who is older, Fred or Alfonzo?

Solve by answering 7 to 12.

7. How many days are in a year?   __365__

8. Do you need to multiply or divide to change years to days?   __multiply__

9. What is (2 × 365) + 10?   __740__

10. How many days are two years and ten days?   __740__

Name _____

Intervention
Lesson **138**

More Units of Time (continued)

11. Compare. Write >, <, or =.   2 years 10 days $<$ 745 days

12. Who is older, Fred or Alfonzo?   __Alfonzo__

13. **Reasoning** Find the missing numbers.

    75 minutes = __1__ hour, __15__ minutes

Compare. Write >, <, or =.

14. 2 minutes $<$ 126 seconds

15. 4 weeks $=$ 28 days

16. 2 weeks and 3 days $>$ 16 days

17. 50 weeks $=$ 350 days

18. 50 hours $>$ 2 days

19. 208 minutes $<$ 4 hours

20. 2 decades $<$ 34 years

21. 28 months $>$ 2 years

22. 23 weeks $=$ 161 days

23. 6 hours $>$ 150 minutes

Find each missing number.

24. 420 seconds = __7__ minutes

25. 156 weeks = __3__ years

26. 105 days = __15__ weeks

27. 3 hours = __10,800__ seconds

28. **Reasoning** Jerome slept 8 hours and 35 minutes on Tuesday night while Manuel slept 525 minutes. Who slept longer? Explain how you solved it.
    Manuel; Sample answer: 8 hours and 35 minutes equal 515 minutes and 515 < 525.

Objective Students will convert units of time.
Vocabulary Leap year, decade, century, millennium

1 Conceptual Development
Use with Exercises 1–13.

In this lesson you will convert units of time.

Review the units of time in the table, with extra emphasis on *leap year*, *decade*, *century*, and *millennium*. Explain how these terms relate to the units of time students already know. Read the problem aloud with the class. *How will you compare these times?* Convert the hours and minutes to minutes, or convert the minutes to hours and minutes. *What is essential before you compare measurements?* The measurements must be in the same unit before you can compare them. *How do you convert the measurements to be in the same unit?* Multiply if you are going from a larger unit to a smaller unit; divide if you are going from a smaller unit to a larger unit Have students complete Exercises 1–13.

2 Practice Use with Exercises 14–28.

Remind students that time can be measured on a calendar: days, weeks, months, years, leap years. There are also greater units of time: decade, century, and millennium.

Error Intervention If students have difficulty remembering how long a decade, century, or millennium is, have them look up the meaning of the prefix of each term in the dictionary.

If You Have More Time Have students write the age of the United States using centuries, decades, years, months, and days. Assume the country was "born" on July 4, 1776. Check students' work.

3 Assessment

In this lesson students learned to convert units of time. Use the **Quick Check** problem to assess students' understanding.

Quick Check Formative Assessment

Find the missing number: 104 weeks = _____ years 2

MORE ELAPSED TIME

Name _____

Intervention Lesson 139

More Elapsed Time

Elapsed time is the amount of time that passes between the beginning and the end of an event.

Simone's school starts at 8:40 A.M. and ends at 3:45 P.M. How much time does Simone spend at school?

Find the elapsed time that Simone is at school by answering 1 to 7.

1. How much time passes from 8:40 to 9:00? — **20 minutes**

2. How much time passes from 9:00 to 12:00? — **3 hours**

3. How much time passes from 12:00 to 3:00? — **3 hours**

4. How much time passes from 3:00 to 3:45? — **45 minutes**

5. What is 20 minutes + 3 hours + 3 hours + 45 minutes? — **6 hours 65 min**

6. What is 65 minutes in hours and minutes? — **1 hour 5 min**

7. How much time does Simone spend at school? — **7 hours 5 min**

After school Simone spends 20 minutes walking home and she has 30 minutes before she must leave for soccer practice. What time must she leave for soccer practice?

Find the end time by answering 8 to 10.

8. School ends at 3:45 P.M. If Simone spends 20 minutes walking home, what time does she arrive at home? — **4:05 P.M.**

139 (student p. 1) MDIS 2.0

Name _____

Intervention Lesson 139

More Elapsed Time (continued)

9. Simone must leave for practice 30 minutes later. What time is it 30 minutes after 4:05? — **4:35 P.M.**

10. What time must Simone leave for soccer practice? — **4:35 P.M.**

11. Start: 3:05 A.M. Finish: 5:37 A.M. — **2 h 32 min**

12. Start: 10:45 A.M. Finish: 3:07 P.M. — **4 h 22 min**

13. Start: 4:58 P.M. Finish: 6:56 P.M. — **1 h 58 min**

Write the time each clock will show in 38 minutes.

14. — **3:47**

15. — **9:20**

Write the time each clock will show in 3 hours and 35 minutes

16. — **6:25**

17. — **5:10**

Find each start or finish time.

18. Start: 2:24 P.M.
    Elapsed time: 3 hours and 32 minutes
    Finish: **5:56 P.M.**

19. Start: **10:35 A.M.**
    Elapsed time: 55 minutes
    Finish: 11:30 A.M.

20. A theater started a movie promptly at 6:30 P.M. If the movie finished at 8:22 P.M., how long was the movie? — **1 hour, 52 min**

139 (student p. 2) MDIS 2.0

Objective Students will calculate elapsed time.
Vocabulary Elapsed time

1 Conceptual Development
Use with Exercises 1–10.

In this lesson you will learn to calculate elapsed time.

Explain that students will be calculating *elapsed time.* Have students read the problem at the top of the page. *What is elapsed time?* The time that passes between the beginning and the end of an event *Why do you count the number of minutes from 8:40 to 9:00 first?* It is easier to count hours from times that are on the hour. Have students complete Exercises 1–7. *Why do you split the times 9:00–12:00 and then 12:00–3:00?* 12:00 is when the numbers start over and the time changes from A.M. to P.M. *Why do you count minutes again at the end?* The end time is not on the hour. *How do you find the total time?* Add each partial time *Why do you need to convert 65 minutes?* There are 60 minutes in an hour, so when the minutes are more than 60, they need to be changed to hours and minutes. Have students complete Exercises 8–10.

2 Practice Use with Exercises 11–20.

Have students practice skip counting from one time to another using intervals of minutes, 5 minutes, and hours.

Error Intervention If students have difficulty finding the start time given the finish time and elapsed time, have them use a model clock and move the hands backward.

If You Have More Time Have students write elapsed time problems about activities in their lives for other students to solve. Check students' work.

3 Assessment

In this lesson students learned to calculate elapsed time. Use the **Quick Check** problem to assess students' understanding.

Quick Check — Formative Assessment

Find the finish time given the following: Start time is 6:54 A.M., and elapsed time is 2 hours 13 minutes. 9:07 A.M.

Elapsed Time in Other Units

Salvador went to bed at 10:40 P.M. and woke up at a quarter to 8 the next morning. How many hours did Salvador sleep?

One way to find the elapsed time is with a number line.

Find the elapsed time by answering 1 to 6.

Elapsed Time

10:40

```
10:00  11:00  12:00  1:00  2:00  3:00  4:00  5:00  6:00  7:00  8:00
P.M.          A.M.                                              A.M.
```

1. Label each of the tick marks on the number line.

2. Plot and label a point on the number line that represents 10:40 P.M.

3. What time is a quarter to 8 in the morning? __7:45 A.M.__

4. Make jumps of length one hour on the number line, until you get close to 7:45, without going past it. How many jumps did you make? __9__

5. Draw a small jump to 7:45 A.M.
   How much time is represented by all the jumps? __9__ h __5__ min

6. How many hours did Salvador sleep? __9__ h __5__ min

Another way to find elapsed time is to subtract.
End Time − Start Time = Elapsed Time

Find the elapsed time another way by answering 7 to 14.

```
        11 h |60| min
        12 h 00 min
      − 10 h 40 min
        1 h 20 min
```

7. Subtract to find the elapsed time before midnight.
   12 hours is the same as 11 hours and how many minutes?
   12 h = 11 h __60__ min
   Rename 12 hours 00 minutes at the right.

8. Subtract the minutes and record at the right.   60 min − 40 min = __20__ min

9. Subtract the hours and record at the right.   11 h − 10 h = __1__ h

10. How long did Salvador sleep before midnight?   __1__ h __20__ min

11. How long did Salvador sleep after midnight?   __7__ h __45__ min

Elapsed Time in Other Units (continued)

12. Add the elapsed time before midnight to the elapsed time after midnight to find the total elapsed time. Record at the right.

   20 min + 45 min = __65__ min   1 h + 7 h = __8__ h

```
  1 h 20 min
+ 7 h 45 min
  8 h 65 min
```

13. Rename 8 hours 65 minutes.

   65 minutes = __1__ h __5__ min   8 hours 65 minutes = __9__ h __5__ min

14. How many hours did Salvador sleep?   __9__ h __5__ min

Find each elapsed time.

15. 9:15 A.M. to 4:05 P.M.
    6 h 50 min

16. Quarter to 8 in the evening to 2:30 A.M.
    6 h 45 min

17. 1:26 P.M. to 5:56 A.M.
    16 h 30 min

18. Quarter after 12 noon to 9:30 P.M.
    9 h 15 min

Find each start or end time.

19. Start: 10:24 P.M.
    Elapsed time: 3 h and 41 min
    Finish: __2:05 A.M.__

20. Start: __3:35 P.M.__
    Elapsed time: 12 h 55 min
    Finish: 4:30 A.M.

Add or subtract.

21.   6 h 20 min
    − 3 h 40 min
      2 h 40 min

22.   3 h 38 min
    + 6 h 47 min
     10 h 25 min

23.   2 h 39 min
    +   56 min
      3 h 35 min

24.   5 h 10 min
    − 2 h 55 min
      2 h 15 min

25.   5 h 24 min
    + 3 h 41 min
      9 h 5 min

26.   1 h 35 min
    −   56 min
          39 min

27. **Reasoning** An airplane takes off at 11:50 P.M. and lands at 8:12 A.M. How long was the plane in the air?
    8 h 22 min

Objective Students will calculate elapsed time.
Vocabulary Elapsed time

① Conceptual Development
Use with Exercises 1–14.

In this lesson you will learn to calculate elapsed time.

Show students a number line that can be used to calculate *elapsed time.* How will you label the number line? With times on the hour; After 12:00, the times will start with 1:00 A.M. How can you locate 10:40 P.M.? It is between 10:00 P.M. and 11:00 P.M. but closer to 11:00 P.M. How can you use jumps to calculate the elapsed time? Jump from 10:40 P.M. to 11:00 P.M., then jump from 11:00 P.M. to 7:00 A.M. by the hour, and then make a final jump from 7:00 A.M. to 7:45 A.M. Have students complete Exercises 1–6. Explain that they can also add or subtract time when solving elapsed time problems. Have students read Exercise 7. Why must you regroup to subtract 10:40 from 12:00? You cannot subtract 40 minutes from 0 minutes. Have students complete Exercises 7–14.

② Practice Use with Exercises 15–27.

Practice finding differences using a number line. Be sure students understand that they are counting the spaces between the two numbers, not the hash marks.

Error Intervention If students have difficulty regrouping when subtracting times, remind them that when they regroup one hour, it becomes 60 minutes.

If You Have More Time Have students use a movie theater's schedule to calculate the elapsed time between the start times of a movie they want to see. Check students' work.

③ Assessment

In this lesson students learned to calculate elapsed time. Use the **Quick Check** problem to assess students' understanding.

Quick Check  **Formative Assessment**

Find the elapsed time given the following: Start time is 3:39 P.M., and finish time is 10:02 P.M.
6 hours 23 minutes

PERIMETER

Perimeter

Materials crayons or markers, centimeter ruler for each student.

Find the perimeter of the figure at the right by answering 1 to 3. **Perimeter** is the distance around a figure. Each space between lines equals 1 unit.

I unit   2 units

1. Trace the figure with a crayon or marker. Count the number of spaces as you trace.

2. How many spaces did you trace? __12__

3. What is the perimeter of the figure? __12__ units

scale: I—I = I unit

You can also find the perimeter by adding the lengths of the sides.

Find the perimeter of the figure to the right by answering 4 to 6.

4. How many sides does this figure have? __6__

5. Trace over the sides as you count and record the length of each side. Order of answers may vary.

__3__ + __5__ + __5__ + __3__ + __2__ + __2__ = __20__

scale: ·—· = I meter

6. What is the perimeter of the figure? __20__ meters

Find the perimeter of the rectangle by answering 7 to 8.

Opposite sides of a rectangle have equal lengths.

7. Record the length of the sides. Find the sum.

10 + 3 + __10__ + __3__ = __16__

10 cm

3 cm

8. What is the perimeter of the rectangle? __16__ cm

141 (student p. 1)   MDIS 2.0

Perimeter (continued)

9. **Reasoning** Use a ruler to measure each side of the figure in inches. What is the perimeter of the figure?

__10 in.__

Find the perimeter of each figure.

10.

__18 units__

11.

__30 units__

12.
3 in.   5 in.
4 in.
__12 in.__

13. 5 cm
1 cm   1 cm
5 cm
__12 cm__

14. 9 cm
9 cm
__36 cm__

15.
5 cm   5 cm
6 cm
6 cm   6 cm
__28 cm__

16. **Reasoning** If the length of one side of a square is 3 inches, what is the perimeter of the square? Explain your answer.

The lengths of the sides of a square are all the same. Therefore the perimeter is 3 + 3 + 3 + 3 = 12 inches.

141 (student p. 2)   MDIS 2.0

Objective Students will calculate the perimeter.
Vocabulary Perimeter
Materials Crayons or markers, centimeter ruler for each student

① Conceptual Development
Use with Exercises 1–9.

In this lesson you will learn to calculate the perimeter.

Explain that the distance around a figure is called the *perimeter. How do you find the length of a line on a grid?* Count the number of spaces long it is *How can you find the perimeter of the first figure?* Count the number of spaces all the way around it Have students complete Exercises 1–3. Explain that there is another way to find perimeter. *If you know the length of each side, how do you find perimeter?* Add the lengths of each side Have students complete Exercises 4–6. Have students look at the rectangle at the bottom of the page. *Why are the lengths of only two sides of the rectangle given?* Because opposite sides of a rectangle have equal lengths *How many sides will you add to find the perimeter of a rectangle?* 4 Have students complete Exercises 7–9.

② Practice Use with Exercises 10–16.

Point out that some of the figures have more than four sides. Students need to add the lengths of all sides to find the perimeter.

Error Intervention If students have difficulty remembering which sides they have added, have them highlight the side once it has been added.

If You Have More Time Have students find the perimeter of different objects in the room using different units of measure based on the size. Check students' work.

③ Assessment

In this lesson students learned to calculate the perimeter. Use the **Quick Check** problem to assess students' understanding.

Quick Check **Formative** Assessment

The side of an equilateral triangle measures 5 mm. What is the perimeter of the triangle? 15 mm

MDIS 2.0

Exploring Area

Use square pattern blocks to cover each shape. Write the number of squares you used.

1. __6__ square units

2. __5__ square units Blue

3. __8__ square units Red

4. Color the shape with the greatest area red. Color the shape with the least area blue. How did you decide which shape had the greatest area?
The third shape has the greatest area because 8 is greater than 6 or 5.

Exploring Area (continued)

Find the area of each shape.

5.

area: __20__ square units

6.

area: __6__ square units

7.

area: __11__ square units

8.

area: __11__ square units

9. **Reasoning** Color two different shapes with an area of 10 square units. Use 2 colors.

Answers may vary.

Objective Students will find the area of shapes.
Vocabulary Area
Materials Pattern block squares or cut-out squares that are $\frac{3}{4}$ inch on a side, up to 8 per student; crayons or markers

① Conceptual Development
Use with Exercises 1–4.

In this lesson you will learn to find the area of shapes.

Explain that *area* can be measured by covering a figure with squares. Show how to cover the first shape using squares. *How many squares does it take to cover the first shape?* 6 *What units come after the 6?* Square units Have students complete Exercises 1–4. *Which shape has the greatest area?* The third shape *How do you know?* It takes the most squares to cover it. Have students color the shape with the greatest area red. *Which shape has the least area?* The second shape *How do you know?* It takes the fewest squares to cover it. Have students color the shape with the least area blue.

② Practice Use with Exercises 5–9.

Tell students to find the area of each shape by counting the squares.

Error Intervention If students have difficulty distinguishing area from perimeter, have them shade the area of a shape blue and trace the perimeter in red.

If You Have More Time Have students make block letters on grid paper and find the area of each letter. Check students' work.

③ Assessment

In this lesson students learned to find the area of shapes. Use the **Quick Check** problem to assess students' understanding.

Quick Check   Formative Assessment

Draw a rectangle on the board with a grid shows 3 rows and 6 columns. *What is the area of the rectangle?* 18 square units

FINDING AREA ON A GRID

Name _____

Finding Area on a Grid

Materials crayons or markers

Area is the number of square units needed to cover the region inside a figure.

Find the area of the rectangle by answering 1 and 2.

1. Color each grid square inside the rectangle. Count as you color. How many grid squares did you color? __12__

2. What is the area of the rectangle?

   __12__ square units

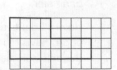

☐ = I square unit

Find the area of the polygon by answering 3 and 4.

3. Color each grid square inside the polygon. Count as you color. How many grid squares did you color? __24__

4. What is the area of the polygon? __24__ square feet

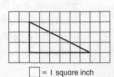

☐ = I square foot

Estimate the area of the triangle by answering 5 to 8.

5. Color the whole squares blue. How many squares did you color? __6__

6. Combine partial square to make whole squares. Color the partial squares red. The partial squares make up about how many whole squares? __3__

7. Add. 6 + 3 = __9__

☐ = I square inch

8. What is the estimated area of the triangle?

   __9__ square inches

143 (student p. 1) MDIS 2.0

Name _____

Finding Area on a Grid (continued)

Find each area. Write your answer in square units.

9.

   __5__ square units

10.

    __9__ square units

11.

    __7__ square units

Find each area. Write your answer in square units.

12.

    __10__ square units

13.

    __10__ square units

14.

    __15__ square units

Judy baked several different shapes of crackers and wants to know which is largest. Each cracker was placed on a grid. Estimate the area of each cracker in Exercises 15 to 17.

15. Triangle

    __about 4__ square units

16. Hexagon

    __about 6__ square units

17. Quadrilateral

    __about 5__ square units

18. Which cracker in Exercises 15–17 has the greatest area? Exercise 16, the hexagon-shaped cracker

143 (student p. 2) MDIS 2.0

Objective Students will find area on a grid.
Vocabulary Area
Materials Crayons or markers

① Conceptual Development
Use with Exercises 1–8.

In this lesson you will learn to find area on a grid.

Explain to students that they can use a grid to find the area of a figure. Have students complete Exercises 1–2. *What are the units for the next figure?* Square feet Show students how large one square foot is. Have students complete Exercises 3–4. *Why do you need to estimate the area of the next figure?* There are some partial squares shaded. *What does each square represent?* 1 square inch Have students complete Exercises 5–8.

② Practice Use with Exercises 9–18.

Make a connection between the squares on the grid and the pattern block squares that students used to find the area of figures in Intervention Lesson 142. Each square, whether a block or on the grid, represents one square unit of area.

Error Intervention If students have difficulty finding area on the grid, have them write the number in each square as it is counted.

If You Have More Time Have students draw a figure on a grid and write the area on the back of the piece of paper. Then have them exchange the drawing with a partner and have the partner find the area of the figure. Check students' work.

③ Assessment

In this lesson students learned to find area on a grid. Use the **Quick Check** problem to assess students' understanding.

Quick Check ❧ Formative Assessment

Draw the trapezoid shown on the board. *What is the area of the trapezoid?* 10 square units

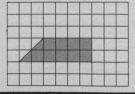

Student Page 1

Name _____

Intervention Lesson **144**

More Perimeter

Jonah's pool is a rectangle. The pool is 15 feet long and 10 feet wide. What is the perimeter of the pool?

Find the perimeter of the pool by answering 1 to 3.

1. Write in the missing measurements on the pool shown at the right.

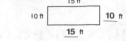
15 ft
10 ft | 10 ft
15 ft

2. Add the lengths of the sides.
10 ft + _10_ ft + 15 ft + _15_ ft = _50_ ft

3. What is the perimeter of the pool? _50_ ft

Find a formula for the perimeter of a rectangle by answering 4 to 10.

Rectangle A   3 in.
8 in.

Rectangle B   4 ft
5 ft

4. Write the side lengths of the rectangle.
8 + 3 + _8_ + 3 = _22_ in.

5. Rearrange the numbers.
8 + 8 + 3 + _3_ = _22_ in.

6. Rewrite the number sentence.
2(8) + 2 (_3_) = _22_ in.
16 + _6_ = _22_ in.

7. Write the side lengths of the rectangle.
5 + 4 + _5_ + _4_ = _18_ ft

8. Rearrange the numbers.
5 + 5 + _4_ + _4_ = _18_ ft

9. Rewrite the number sentence.
2(5) + 2(_4_) = _18_ ft
8 + _10_ = _18_ ft

10. Complete the table.

Rectangle	Length	Width	Perimeter
A	8	3	2(_8_) + 2(3)
B	5	4	2(5) + 2(4)
Any	ℓ	w	$2\ell + 2$ _w_

144 (student p. 1)   MDIS 2.0

Student Page 2

Name _____

Intervention Lesson **144**

More Perimeter (continued)

The formula for the perimeter of a rectangle is $P = 2\ell + 2w$

11. **Reasoning** Use the formula to find the perimeter of Jonah's pool.

$P = \quad 2\ell \ + \ 2w$
$\quad\quad \downarrow \quad\quad \downarrow$
$P = 2(\_15\_) + 2(\_10\_) = \_30\_ + \_20\_ = \_50\_$ ft

12. Is the perimeter the same as you found on the previous page? _yes_

A square is a type of rectangle where all of the side lengths are equal.

Find a formula for the perimeter of the square by answering 13 to 15.

13. Add to find the perimeter of the square shown at the right.

_5_ + _5_ + _5_ + _5_ = _20_

5 cm

14. What could you multiply to find the perimeter of the square? _4 × 5_

15. If s equals the length of a side of a square, how could you find the perimeter? $P = \_4s\_$

Find the perimeter of the rectangle with the given dimensions.

16. $\ell = 9$ mm, $w = 12$ mm
_42 mm_

17. $\ell = 13$ in., $w = 14$ in.
_54 in._

18. $\ell = 2$ ft, $w = 15$ ft
_34 ft_

19. $\ell = 17$ cm, $w = 25$ cm
_84 cm_

Find the perimeter of the square with the given side.

20. $s = 2$ yd
_8 yd_

21. $s = 10$ in.
_40 in._

22. $s = 31$ km
_124 km_

23. $s = 11$ m
_44 m_

24. **Reasoning** Could you use the formula for the perimeter of a rectangle to find the perimeter of a square? Explain your reasoning.
Yes; the formula for the perimeter of a rectangle can be used to find the perimeter of a square because a square is a rectangle.

144 (student p. 2)   MDIS 2.0

Teacher Notes

Objective Students will use formulas to find perimeter.
Vocabulary Perimeter, formula

① Conceptual Development
Use with Exercises 1–15.

In this lesson you will learn to use formulas to find perimeter.

Have students read the problem at the top of the page. Revisit the term *perimeter* as needed. Have students complete Exercises 1–3. Explain that students can also use a *formula* to find the perimeter of a rectangle. *What is the perimeter of a rectangle?* The distance around the rectangle Have students complete Exercises 4–10. *Using words, what is the formula for the perimeter of a rectangle?* Perimeter equals 2 times the length plus 2 times the width Have students complete Exercises 11–15.

② Practice Use with Exercises 16–24.

Remind students to multiply 2 times the length and 2 times the width and then add the two products to find the perimeter.

Error Intervention If students have difficulty finding perimeters, provide them with cubes and allow them to model each rectangle.

If You Have More Time Have students solve the following problem and explain their methods: *I have a rectangle with a perimeter of 20 inches. The length is 5 inches. What is the width? What does this tell you about the rectangle?* 5 inches; The figure is a square.

③ Assessment

In this lesson students learned to use formulas to find perimeter. Use the **Quick Check** problem to assess students' understanding.

Quick Check **Formative** Assessment

A rectangle has a length of 7 inches and a width of 9 inches. What is the perimeter? 32 inches

---

Name _____

Intervention
Lesson **145**

Area of Rectangles and Squares

Maria's flower garden is in the shape of rectangle that measures 6 feet long and 4 feet wide. What is the area of the garden?

Find a formula for area of a rectangle by answering 1 to 6.

1. The rectangle at the right is a model of the garden. How many squares are in the model? __24__

2. What is the area of the garden? __24__ square feet

3. What is the length of the garden? __6__ feet

4. What is the width of the garden? __4__ feet

5. What could you multiply to find the area of the garden? __6 × 4__

6. Find the area of each rectangle by counting squares. Write the area in the table below. Complete the table.

Rectangle A — 4 cm, 7 cm

Rectangle B — 3 in., 6 in.

Rectangle	Area	Length	Width	Product
Maria's garden	24	6	4	6 × 4
A	28	7	4	7 × _4_
B	18	6	3	_6_ × _3_
Any	Any	ℓ	w	ℓ × _w_

Name _____

Intervention
Lesson **145**

Area of Rectangles and Squares (continued)

The formula for the area of a rectangle is $A = \ell \times w$ or $A = \ell w$.

7. **Reasoning** Use the formula to find the area of a rectangle that is 8 meters long and 5 meters wide.

$$A = \quad \ell \quad \times \quad w$$
$$\downarrow \qquad \downarrow$$
$$A = (\underline{8}) \times (\underline{5}) = \underline{40} \text{ square meters}$$

A square is a type of rectangle where all of the side lengths are equal.

Find a formula for the area of the square shown by answering 8 and 9.

8. Use the formula $A = \ell w$ to find the area of the square.

__8__ × __8__ = __64__ mm²

 8 mm

9. If s equals the length of a side of a square, how could you find the area of any square? $A = $ __s × s__

Find the area of each figure.

10. 7 in., 7 in., 7 in., 7 in.

11. 5 cm, 3 cm

12. 2 km, 14 km

__49 in.²__   __15 cm²__   __28 km²__

Find the area of the rectangle with the given dimensions.

13. $\ell = 15$ mm, $w = 4$ mm   14. $\ell = 3$ cm, $w = 10$ cm
    __60 mm²__   __30 cm²__

15. **Reasoning** The area of a square is 81 square feet. What is the length of each side?   __9 ft__

16. **Reasoning** Using only whole numbers, what are all the possible dimensions of a rectangle with an area of 12 square centimeters?
1 cm by 12 cm; 2 cm by 6 cm; 3 cm by 4 cm

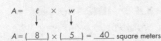

Objective Students will find the area of rectangles and squares.
Vocabulary Area, formula

① Conceptual Development
Use with Exercises 1–9.

In this lesson you will learn to find the area of rectangles and squares.

Have students read the problem at the top of the page. Revisit the terms *area* and *formula* as needed. Have students complete Exercises 1–6. *What is the area of a rectangle?* The amount of space the rectangle covers *Do you find counting all of the squares easier or harder than multiplying the length times the width?* Answers may vary; Try to help students understand that multiplying is easier when they are finding a large area, such as the classroom floor. Have students complete Exercises 7–9.

② Practice Use with Exercises 10–16.

Remind students to multiply the length by the width to find the area of a rectangle or square.

Error Intervention If students have difficulty finding areas, allow them to use pattern block squares to practice covering shapes to find the area.

If You Have More Time Have students solve the following problem and explain their methods: *I have a rectangle with an area of 49 square inches. The length is 7 inches. What is the width? What does this tell you about the rectangle?* 7 inches; The rectangle is a square.

③ Assessment

In this lesson students learned to find the area of rectangles and squares. Use the **Quick Check** problem to assess students' understanding.

Quick Check  **Formative** Assessment

A rectangle has a length of 8 inches and a width of 12 inches. What is the area? 96 square inches

---

MDIS 2.0

Name _____

Area of Irregular Figures

Materials crayons or markers

Find the area of the irregular figure on the right.

1. How many squares are there? _21_

2. What is the area of the figure? _21_ square meters

You can also find the area of the figure by breaking it into 2 rectangles and then finding the sum of the areas of the 2 rectangles.

scale: ☐ = 1 meter

3. What is the area of Rectangle 1?

   $A = \ell \times w$

   $A = 2 \times$ _3_ = _6_ sq meters

Rectangle 1→

4. What is the area of Rectangle 2?

   $A = \ell \times w$

   $A = 3 \times$ _5_ = _15_ sq meters

←Rectangle 2

5. What is the sum of the two areas?

   Area of Rectangle 1 + Area of Rectangle 2 = Total Area

       6   + _15_   = _21_ sq meters

6. Is the area the same as the one you found by counting? _yes_

Find the area of the shaded figure below by answering 7 to 12.

7. Divide the figure into 2 rectangles and a square.

8. What is the area of Rectangle 1?

   $5 \times$ _8_ = _40_ sq cm

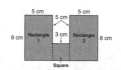

146 (student p. 1)   MDIS 2.0

Name _____

Area of Irregular Figures (continued)

9. What is the area of Rectangle 2? $5 \times$ _8_ = _40_ sq cm

10. What is the area of the square? $3 \times$ _3_ = _9_ sq cm

11. Add the areas of the three smaller figures.

   Rectangle 1 + Rectangle 2 +   Square   = Total Area

   _40_ sq cm + 40 sq cm + _9_ sq cm = _89_ sq cm

12. What is the area of the figure? _89_ sq cm

13.

    _____18 m²_____

14.

    _____20 ft²_____

15.

    _____124 in.²_____

16.

    _____51 in.²_____

17.

    _____56 ft²_____

18.

    _____150 yd²_____

19. Bob wants to carpet the room shown. How many square yards of carpet will he need? _32 yd²_

20. **Reasoning** How could you use subtraction to find the area of the figure below?

    You could use subtraction by finding the area of the larger square which is 144 square feet and then subtracting the area of the cut out section which is 5 × 4 = 20 square feet. 144 − 20 = 124 ft²

146 (student p. 2)   MDIS 2.0

Objective Students will find the area of irregular figures.
Materials Crayons or markers

① Conceptual Development
Use with Exercises 1–12.

In this lesson you will learn to find the area of irregular figures.

Explain that some figures are irregular shapes, so you cannot find their areas by simply multiplying length by width. Have students preview the lesson by looking at the diagrams. *What are two ways you will find the area in this lesson?* By counting squares and by dividing the irregular shape into rectangles and squares and finding the area of each part Have students complete Exercises 1–6. *How did you divide the irregular shape?* Into 2 rectangles Have students complete Exercises 7–12.

② Practice Use with Exercises 13–20.

Encourage students to ask themselves where they can draw a line in order to create a rectangle.

Error Intervention If students have difficulty dividing irregular figures into rectangles and squares, have them cut out irregular figures similar to the ones in this lesson. Then have them cut each figure into rectangles and squares.

If You Have More Time Have students solve the following problem: *Explain why, when you make an irregular shape into smaller rectangles, you sometimes have to calculate the measurement of a length or width.* Check students' answers.

③ Assessment

In this lesson students learned to find the area of irregular figures. Use the **Quick Check** problem to assess students' understanding.

Quick Check **Formative** Assessment

Have students look at the irregular shape on the bottom of the first page. Ask them to find the area of the irregular figure made up of Rectangle 1 and the square. 49 square centimeters

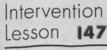

Name _____

Intervention
Lesson **147**

Rectangles with the Same Area or Perimeter

Materials colored pencils or crayons.

Ms. Arellano's class is making a sand box shaped like a rectangle for the kindergarten class. They have 16 feet of wood to put around the sand box. What length and width should the sand box be so it has the greatest area?

Each of the rectangles in the grid at the right has a perimeter of 16 feet. Find which rectangle has the greatest area by answering 1 to 3.

1. Complete the table. The formula for area of a rectangle is $A = \ell \times w$.

Rectangle	Length	Width	Area (square units)
W	7	1	7
X	6	2	12
Y	5	3	15
Z	4	4	16

2. What are the length and width of the rectangle with the greatest area? ___4 ft by 4 ft___

3. What length and width should Ms. Arellano's class use for the sand box? ___4 ft by 4 ft___

4. **Reasoning** Tracy told Tomas that if a two rectangles have the same perimeter, they have the same area. Is Tracy correct? Explain your reasoning.
   Tracy is not correct. All of the rectangles in the grid above have the same perimeter, but none have the same area.

Mr. Katz has 30 carpet squares to make a reading area in his classroom. Each square is one foot on a side. He wants to make the area in the shape of a rectangle with the least possible border. How should he arrange the carpet squares?

147 (student p. 1) MDIS 2.0

Name _____

Intervention
Lesson **147**

Rectangles with the Same Area or Perimeter (continued)

Each of the rectangles on the grid at the right has an area of 30 square feet. Find which one has the least perimeter by answering 5 to 8.

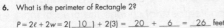

5. What is the perimeter of Rectangle 1?
   $P = 2\ell + 2w = 2(\underline{6}) + 2(5)$
   $= \underline{12} + \underline{10} = \underline{22}$ feet

6. What is the perimeter of Rectangle 2?
   $P = 2\ell + 2w = 2(\underline{10}) + 2(3) = \underline{20} + \underline{6} = \underline{26}$ feet

7. What is the length and width of the rectangle with the least perimeter? ___6 ft by 5 ft___

8. How should Mr. Katz arrange the carpet squares? ___in a 6 ft by 5 ft array___

Draw a rectangle with the same area as the one shown. Then find the perimeter of each.

Answers may vary. Possible answers are given.

9.
   P = 12 in.
   2 in.
   4 in.

   ___8 in. by 1 in.;___
   ___P = 18 in.___

10. P = 18 cm
    3 cm
    6 cm

    ___9 cm by 2 cm;___
    ___P = 22 cm___

11.
    P = 22 m
    4 m
    7 m

    ___14 m by 2 m;___
    ___P = 32 m___

12. **Reasoning** Marco has 36 feet of fencing, what is the greatest area that can he can fence? ___81 ft²___

147 (student p. 2) MDIS 2.0

Objective Students will find rectangles with the same area or perimeter.
Vocabulary Area, perimeter
Materials Crayons or colored pencils

❶ Conceptual Development
Use with Exercises 1–8.

In this lesson you will learn to find rectangles with the same area or perimeter.

Have students read the problem at the top of the page. Revisit the terms *area* and *perimeter* as needed. Have students complete Exercises 1–4. **How can the perimeters all be the same but the areas be different?** The distance around each rectangle is the same, but because of the different layouts of each sandbox, the area that is being covered by each is different. **Have students complete Exercises 5–8.**

❷ Practice **Use with Exercises 9–12.**

Review the definitions of area and perimeter.

Error Intervention If students have difficulty finding rectangles with the same area, suggest that they use graph paper. Tell them to create a rectangle with a different shape but the same number of squares.

If You Have More Time Have students use a piece of string or yarn to make different shapes with the same perimeter. Ask them to describe what happens to the area as the shape becomes very long and narrow. The area gets smaller.

❸ Assessment

In this lesson students learned to find rectangles with the same area or perimeter. Use the **Quick Check** problem to assess students' understanding.

Quick Check **Formative Assessment**

Draw two rectangles with the same area but different perimeters. Check students' work.

Name _____

Area of Parallelograms

Materials grid paper, colored pencils or markers, scissors

Find the area of the parallelogram on the grid by answering 1 to 10.

1. Trace the parallelogram below on a piece of grid paper. Then cut out the parallelogram.

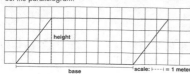

2. Cut out the right triangle created by the dashed line.

3. Take the right triangle and move it to the right of the parallelogram.

4. What shape did you create? __a rectangle__

5. Is the area of the parallelogram the same as the area of the rectangle? __yes__

6. What is the area of the rectangle? $A = \ell \times w =$ __10__ × 4 = __40__ sq meters

7. What is the base b of the parallelogram? __10__ meters

8. What is the height h of the parallelogram? __4__ meters

9. What is the base times the height of the parallelogram? __40__

10. Is this the same as the area of the rectangle? __yes__

148 (student p. 1)   MDIS 2.0

Name _____

Area of Parallelograms (continued)

The formula for the area of a parallelogram is $A = bh$.

11. Use the formula to find the area of a parallelogram with a base of 9 ft and a height of 6 feet.

$A = \quad b \quad \times \quad h$

$A = (\underline{9}) \times (\underline{6}) = \underline{54}$ square feet

Find the area of each figure.

12.

__300 m²__

13.

__80 hm²__

14.

__50 ft²__

15.

__7.5 in.²__

16.

__77 in.²__

17.

__27.9 m²__

18.

__90 mm²__

19.

__84 ft²__

20.

__45 m²__

21. **Reasoning** The area of a parallelogram is 100 square millimeters. The base is 4 millimeters. Find the height.

__25 mm__

148 (student p. 2)   MDIS 2.0

Objective Students will find the area of parallelograms.
Vocabulary Parallelogram, right triangle
Materials Grid paper, colored pencils or markers, scissors

1 Conceptual Development
Use with Exercises 1–11.

In this lesson you will learn to find the area of parallelograms.

Revisit the terms *parallelogram* and *right triangle* as needed. Have students complete Exercises 1–4. *What shape did you create?* A rectangle *Did moving the right triangle change the area or the shape?* It only changed the shape. *What shape would you make if the base and the height of the parallelogram were the same?* You would make a square. Have students complete Exercises 5–11.

2 Practice Use with Exercises 12–21.

Remind students that they need to use only the base and the height of the parallelogram to find the area.

Error Intervention If students have difficulty finding the area of parallelograms, provide them with tangram shapes to help them see how the parallelograms are actually formed by right triangles and rectangles.

If You Have More Time Have students answer the following: *Explain why moving the right triangle does not change the area of the parallelogram.* The area is still the same because the right triangle is still covering up the same amount of space.

3 Assessment

In this lesson students learned to find the area of parallelograms. Use the **Quick Check** problem to assess students' understanding.

Quick Check   **Formative Assessment**

What is the area of a parallelogram with a base of 11 cm and a height of 6 cm? 66 cm²

AREA OF TRIANGLES

Materials markers, crayons or colored pencils

Jerah is making a model of a sailboat. The sail of the boat is a triangle. The sail has a base of 4 inches and a height of 3 inches. What is the area of the sail? The triangle below. is a model of the sail.

Find the area of the sail by answering 1 to 5.

1. Color the triangle at the right.

2. How does the area of the triangle compare to the area of the rectangle?

   Area of the triangle = $\frac{1}{2}$ × the area of the rectangle

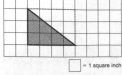
☐ = 1 square inch

3. What is the area of the rectangle? __12__ square inches

4. What is the area of the triangle? __6__ square inches

5. What is the area of Jerah's sail? __6__ square inches

Nina is making a model of a sailboat with a sail in the shape of a triangle like the one shown below. The base of her sail is 7 inches and the height is 4 inches. Find the area of the triangle by answering 6 to 10.

6. Color the triangle at the right.

7. How does the area of the triangle compare to the area of the rectangle?

   Area of the triangle = $\frac{1}{2}$ × the area of the rectangle

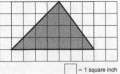
☐ = 1 square inch

8. What is the area of the rectangle? __28__ square inches

9. What is the area of the triangle? __14__ square inches

10. What is the area of Nina's sail? __14__ square inches

149 (student p. 1) MDIS 2.0

---

11. Complete the table.

Triangle	Base	Height	Area
Jerah's sail	4	3	6
Nina's sail	7	4	14
Any	b	h	$\frac{1}{2} \times b \times$ __h__

The formula for the area of a triangle is $A = \frac{1}{2} \times b \times h$ or $A = \frac{1}{2}bh$.

12. **Reasoning** Use the formula to find the area of Jerah's sail.

   $A = \frac{1}{2} \times \quad b \quad \times \quad h$

   $A = \frac{1}{2} \times \underline{4} \times \underline{3} = \underline{12}$ square inches

13. Is the area the same as you found on the previous page? __yes__

Find the area of each figure.

14.
    __21 cm²__

15.
    __56 in.²__

16.
    __54 yd²__

Find the area of the triangle with the measurements shown below. Give the correct units.

17. $b = 22$ yd
    $h = 20$ yd
    __220 yd²__

18. $b = 8$ mm
    $h = 4$ mm
    __16 mm²__

19. $b = 12$ cm
    $h = 4$ cm
    __24 cm²__

20. The front of a tent is in the shape of a triangle with a height of 6 feet and a base of 10 feet. What is the area of the front of the tent?
    __30 ft²__

149 (student p. 2) MDIS 2.0

⏱

Objective Students will find the area of triangles.
Vocabulary Triangle
Materials Markers, crayons, or colored pencils

① Conceptual Development
Use with Exercises 1–13.

In this lesson you will learn to find the area of triangles.

Read the problem at the top of the page aloud. Have students complete Exercises 1–5. *How did you figure out the area of the triangle even though some of the squares were only half used?* By finding the area of the rectangle shown on the grid and then taking half of that area Have students read the next problem and study the figure. *How can the same rule for finding the area of a triangle apply to this triangle even though it is not a right triangle?* The triangle is still half of the rectangle, even though it takes up half in a way different from a right triangle. Have students complete Exercises 6–13.

② Practice Use with Exercises 14–20.

Remind students that to find the area of a triangle, you find the area of the rectangle and then divide that area in half.

Error Intervention If students have difficulty finding the area of triangles, provide them with tangram shapes to help them see that a triangle is half of a rectangle.

If You Have More Time Have students solve the following problem and explain their methods: *Use the triangle from Exercises 6–10. Explain why the areas of the triangles that make up the rest of the rectangle should equal the area of the shaded triangle.* Check students' work.

③ Assessment

In this lesson students learned to find the area of triangles. Use the **Quick Check** problem to assess students' understanding.

Quick Check **Formative** Assessment

What is the area of a triangle with a base of 9 cm and a height of 14 cm? 63 cm²

CIRCUMFERENCE

Name _____

Circumference

Materials Round objects, at least 3 for each group; tape measure or ruler and string for each student

Circumference (C) is the distance around a circle.

1. Complete the table for 3 different round objects.
   Answers will vary but last column should be close to 3.14.

Object	Circumference (C)	Diameter (d)	c ÷ d

The last column should be close to π, ≈ 3.14, every time.

If $C \div d = \pi$, then $C = \pi d$.

2. What is the relationship between the diameter (d) and radius (r) of any circle? $d = \underline{2r}$

3. If $C = \pi d$ and $d = 2r$, what is a formula for the circumference using the radius (r)? $C = 2\pi \underline{} r$

Use a formula to find the circumference of each circle to the nearest whole number.

4.   5.
   (10 in.)   (9 in.)

$C = 2 \quad \pi \quad r$ $C = \quad \pi \quad d$
$\downarrow \qquad \downarrow$ $\downarrow \qquad \downarrow$
$C \approx 2 \times 3.14 \times \underline{10}$ $C \approx \underline{3.14} \times \underline{9}$
$C \approx \underline{63}$ inches $C \approx \underline{28}$ inches

150 (student p. 1)   MDIS 2.0

Name _____

Circumference (continued)

Find the circumference of each circle to the nearest whole number.
Use 3.14 or $\frac{22}{7}$ for π.

6.   7. (14 ft)   8. (16 cm)   9. (28 yd)
   (12 m)

   _75 m_   _88 ft_   _50 cm_   _88 yd_

10.   11. (13 mm)   12. (15 ft)   13. (35 m)
    (2 in.)

    _6 in._   _82 mm_   _47 ft_   _110 m_

14. (3.6 cm)   15. (5.7 yd)   16. ($1\frac{1}{2}$ in.)   17. (9.7 ft)

    _11 cm_   _18 yd_   _9 in._   _61 ft_

18. Miranda wants to sew lace around the outside of a pillow.
    The pillow has a diameter of 35 centimeters. How much
    lace does Miranda need?   _about 110 cm_

19. **Reasoning** Find the distance around the figure at the right.
    Round your answer to the nearest whole number

    _33 in._

20. **Reasoning** Write a formula for the circumference (C) of a semicircle.
    πr or $\frac{1}{2}d\pi$

150 (student p. 2)   MDIS 2.0

🕐

Objective Students will find the circumference of circles.
Vocabulary Diameter, radius, circumference
Materials Round objects, at least 3 per group; tape measure or ruler and string for each student

1 Conceptual Development
Use with Exercises 1–5.

In this lesson you will learn to find the circumference of circles.

Review the terms *diameter* and *radius* as needed. Have students read the definition at the top of the page. *What is circumference?* The distance around a circle. Have students complete Exercises 1–3. *What is the diameter of a circle with a radius of 7 inches?* 14 inches *What is the value of π?* About 3.14 Have students complete Exercises 4–5.

2 Practice Use with Exercises 6–20.

Remind students that the radius of a circle is half the length of the diameter and that π is about 3.14.

Error Intervention If students have difficulty finding the circumference of a circle, allow them to use string and a ruler to draw a circle. Have them trace around the outside of the circle with the string and then measure the string.

If You Have More Time Ask students to use a compass (or other tool) to draw a circle and then measure the diameter of the circle with a ruler. Have students use pieces of string to measure the circumference of the circle. Ask students to divide the circumference by the diameter. (The quotient should be about 3.) *What value did you find?* π

3 Assessment

In this lesson students learned to find the circumference of circles. Use the **Quick Check** problem to assess students' understanding.

Quick Check   🌸 **Formative Assessment**

What is the circumference of a circle with a radius of 19 inches? 119.32 inches

---

AREA OF A CIRCLE

Name _____

Area of a Circle

Materials crayons, markers, or colored pencils, grid paper, compass

Sue places a water sprinkler in her yard. It sprays water 5 feet in every direction. What is the area of the lawn the sprinkler waters?

Find a formula for the area of a circle and find the area of the lawn by answering 1 to 8.

1. The sprinkler sprays in a circle. What is the radius of the circle? __5 ft__

Estimated areas may vary, but should be close to the sample answers given.

2. The grid at the right is a diagram of the sprinkler. Color all the whole squares within the circle one color. How many whole squares did you color?

   __68__ whole squares

3. Combine partial squares to estimate whole squares. Color the partial squares, using a different color. The partial squares make up about how many whole squares?

   __12__ whole squares

4. Add. What is a good estimate of the area of the circle? __80__ units

5. Draw circles on grid paper with each radius listed in the table. Estimate the area and complete the table. Use 3.14 for π. Round πr^2 to the nearest whole number.

Estimated Area	Radius (r)	r^2	πr^2
80	5	25	79
26	3	9	28
106	6	36	113

6. Is the estimated area close to πr^2 each time? __yes__

151 (student p. 1) MDIS 2.0

Name _____

Area of a Circle (continued)

The formula for the area of a circle is $A = \pi r^2$.

7. Use the formula to find the area of a circle with radius 5 feet by filling in the blanks at the right. Round to the nearest whole number.

   $A = \pi \quad r^2$

   $A \approx 3.14 \times \underline{25}$

8. What is the approximate area of lawn watered by the sprinkler? Include the correct units.

   $A \approx \underline{79}$

   about __79 sq ft__

Find the area of each circle to the nearest whole number. Use either 3.14 or $\frac{22}{7}$ for π.

9. (28 yd) __615 yd²__

10. (12 m) __452 m²__

11. (16 cm) __201 cm²__

12. (2 in.) __3 in.²__

13. (14 ft) __615 ft²__

14. (15 ft) __177 ft²__

15. (13 mm) __531 mm²__

16. (35 m) __962 mm²__

17. A cement ring the shape of a circle surrounds a flag pole. The ring is 6 meters across. How much sod, to the nearest whole square meter, does it take to cover the area inside the ring? __28 m²__

18. **Reasoning** Chase used 3.14 for π and found the circumference of a circle to be 47.1 feet. Find the area of the circle to the nearest whole number. __177 ft²__

151 (student p. 2) MDIS 2.0

Objective Students will find the area of a circle.
Vocabulary Diameter, radius
Materials Crayons, markers, or colored pencils; grid paper; compass

1 Conceptual Development
Use with Exercises 1–8.

In this lesson you will learn to find the area of a circle.

Review the terms *diameter* and *radius* as needed. Read the problem at the top of the page together. Have students complete Exercises 1–6. *How is the area of a circle like the area of a rectangle?* The area of a circle is the amount of space a circle covers up. *What are two ways that you can find the area of a circle?* Count squares and use the formula Have students complete Exercises 7–8.

2 Practice Use with Exercises 9–18.

Remind students to find area of a circle using πr^2. Caution students that if the diameter is given, they must first divide the diameter by 2 to find the radius. Then they can find the area.

Error Intervention If students have difficulty calculating the area of a circle, remind them that they can use either 3.14 or $\frac{22}{7}$ for π. The calculation might be easier to perform using a decimal or a fraction. For example, if the radius is divisible by 7, it would be easy to multiply the radius squared by $\frac{22}{7}$.

If You Have More Time Have students answer the following question: *What happens to the area of a circle if the diameter is doubled?* The area becomes 4 times as large as the original circle.

3 Assessment

In this lesson students learned to find the area of a circle. Use the **Quick Check** problem to assess students' understanding.

Quick Check Formative Assessment

What is the area of a circle with a radius of 15 cm? Round your answer to the nearest tenth of a square centimeter. 706.5 cm²

Name _____

Intervention
Lesson **152**

Surface Area of Rectangular Prisms

Materials scissors, copy of nets for the square and rectangular prisms from *Teaching Tool Masters*, for each student

The surface area of a rectangular prism is the sum of the areas of all its faces.

How much wrapping paper does it take to cover the box shown at the right, not counting overlap?

Find the surface area of the prism by answering 1 to 7.

1. Cut out and fold the net for a rectangular prism. Use the folded prism to write the length of each edge on the net. Use lengths shown in the prism above. Unfold the net and use it to label the lengths of the edges on the net at the right.

2. What is the area of the top and bottom of the prism?

   $5 \times 2 =$ __10__ in.^{2}

3. What is the area of the side of the prism?

   __6__ $\times$ __2__ $=$ __12__ in.^{2}

4. What is the area of the front and back of the prism?

   __6__ $\times$ __5__ $=$ __30__ in.^{2}

5. Add the areas of all the faces to find the surface area.

   side   side   front   back   top   bottom

   SA $=$ __12__ $+$ __12__ $+$ __30__ $+$ __30__ $+$ __10__ $+$ __10__ $=$ __104__

6. What is the surface area of the prism? __104__ in.^{2}

7. How much wrapping paper does it take to cover the box? __104 in.^{2}__

Name _____

Intervention
Lesson **152**

Surface Area of Rectangular Prisms (continued)

8. Cut out and fold the net for the square prism and use it to find the surface area of the prism at the right.

   side   side   front   back   top   bottom

   SA $=$ __6__ $+$ __6__ $+$ __6__ $+$ __6__ $+$ __4__ $+$ __4__ $=$ __32__ yd^2

Find the surface area of each figure.

9.

   __164__ in.^{2}

10.

    __102__ ft^2

11.

    __148__ in.^{2}

12.

    __144__ cm^2

13.

    __136__ in.^{2}

14.

    __630__ m^2

15. What is the surface area of a rectangular prism that is 9 yards wide, 10 yards long, and 11 yards high?   __598__ yd^2

16. How much wood does it take to make a storage box that is 4 feet square on the bottom and 3 feet high, with a lid? Do not count overlap.   __80__ ft^2

17. **Reasoning** What is the surface area of the cube shown at the right? How could you find the surface area with out using addition?
    384 m^2; Multiply 6 $\times$ 8 $\times$ 8.

---

① Conceptual Development
Use with Exercises 1–8.

In this lesson you will learn to find the surface area of rectangular prisms.

Revisit the term *rectangular prism* and discuss common terms for this type of solid, such as *box*. Read the problem at the top of the page together. Have students complete Exercises 1–4. *How does understanding area help you to find surface area?* Surface area is the area of each face of an object, all added together to cover every face of a 3-dimensional object. *How many faces does a rectangular prism have?* 6 Have students complete Exercises 5–8.

Objective Students will find the surface area of rectangular prisms.
Vocabulary Rectangular prism
Materials Scissors, copy of nets for the square and rectangular prisms from *Teaching Tool Masters* for each student

② Practice Use with Exercises 9–17.

Remind students that they need to find the area of every face of the rectangular prism before they add all the areas together.

Error Intervention If students have difficulty finding the surface area of rectangular prisms, provide them with nets to cut out and measure. Then have them shade each face as they find the area.

If You Have More Time Have students solve the following problem and explain their methods: *How would you find the surface area of a rectangular prism that has all measurements the same length?* This prism would be a cube. I would find the area of one face and multiply it by 6.

③ Assessment

In this lesson students learned to find the surface area of rectangular prisms. Use the **Quick Check** problem to assess students' understanding.

Quick Check   Formative Assessment

What is the surface area of a rectangular prism that is 12 inches high, 3 inches wide, and 8 inches long?
312 in^2

SURFACE AREA

Name _____

Surface Area

Materials scissors, copy of nets for the cylinder, square pyramid, and triangular prism from *Teaching Tool Masters*, for each student

How much aluminum does it take to make a juice can, not counting overlap, if the diameter is 6 centimeters and the height is 12 centimeters?

Find the surface area of a cylinder by answering 1 to 8.

d = 6 cm
h = 12 cm
ℓ = 18.85 cm

1. Cut out and fold the net for a cylinder. Use the folded cylinder to write the diameter and height of the can, on the net. Unfold the net and use it to label those dimensions on the net at the right.

In any prism or cylinder, the top and bottom are bases. The remaining area is called the **lateral surface area**.

2. The lateral surface area of a cylinder makes a rectangle in the net. The width of the rectangle is the height of the cylinder. What is the length of the rectangle in the cylinder? Fold the net to see.

   The length of the rectangle = the ___circumference___ of the base.

3. Use the formula for the circumference of a circle to find the length of the rectangle. Write the length in the net above.

   $C = \pi d \approx$ __3.14__ $\times$ __6__ $\approx$ __18.84 cm__

4. What is the lateral surface area of the cylinder, to the nearest whole number?

   __12__ $\times$ 18.84 $\approx$ __226 cm²__

5. What is the radius of the base of the cylinder?   r = __3__

6. What is the area of each base of the cylinder, to the nearest whole number?

   $A = \pi r^2 \approx$ __3.14__ $\times$ __9__ $\approx$ __28 cm²__

7. What is the approximate surface area of the cylinder?

   base   base   lateral SA

   SA ≈ __28__ + __28__ + __226__ ≈ __282__ cm²

153 (student p. 1)   MDIS 2.0

Name _____

Surface Area (continued)

8. How much aluminum does it take to make a juice can?   __282 cm²__

How much canvas does it take to make the pup tent shown, not counting overlap? Answer 9 to 12 to find the surface area of the triangular prism.

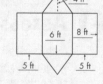
5 ft 4 ft 8 ft 6 ft

9. Cut out and fold the net for a triangular prism. Use the folded prism to write the lengths on the net. Unfold the net and use it to label the lengths on the net at the right.

10. Find the area of each face and write the areas below.

    front   back   bottom   side   side

    SA = __12__ + 12 + __48__ + __40__ + 40

4 ft 6 ft 8 ft 5 ft 5 ft

11. What is the surface area of the triangular prism?   __152__ ft²

12. How much canvas does it take to make the tent?   __152__ ft²

Answer 13 to 15 to find the surface area of the pyramid at the right.

13. Cut out and fold the net for a square pyramid to label the lengths on the net at the right.

    10m 12m 12m

14. Find the area of each face and write the areas below.

    bottom   side   side   side   side

    SA = __144__ + 60 + __60__ + 60 + __60__

    10 m 12 m

15. What is the surface area of the pyramid? __384 m²__

Find the surface area of each solid. Use 3.14 for π.

16.
7 in. 10 in.
__747 in.²__

17. 8 cm 5 cm 7.4 cm 9 cm
__203 cm²__

18.
12 yd 5 yd 5 yd
__145 yd²__

153 (student p. 2)   MDIS 2.0

Objective Students will find the surface area of cylinders, square pyramids, and triangular prisms.
Vocabulary Radius, lateral
Materials Cylindrical object (such as a juice can), scissors, tape, copy of nets for the cylinder, square pyramid, and triangular prism from *Teaching Tool Masters* for each student

① Conceptual Development
Use with Exercises 1–15.

In this lesson you will learn to find the surface area of cylinders, square pyramids, and triangular prisms.

Use the cylindrical object to show students how to visualize the net of a cylinder. Have them cut and tape paper to cover the surfaces and then flatten the paper to make the net. Revisit the term *radius* as needed. Explain that *lateral* means "on the side." Have students complete Exercises 1–8. *How does using a net help you find the surface area of a three-dimensional shape?* The net takes everything from being three-dimensional to being flat, or two-dimensional, so it is easier to calculate the area of each face. Have students complete Exercises 9–15.

② Practice Use with Exercises 16–18.

Remind students to find the area of each face before adding.

Error Intervention
If students have difficulty finding surface areas, encourage them to draw a net for each shape.

If You Have More Time
Have students describe in words the surface area of a cylinder. Twice the area of the base plus the circumference of the base times the height of the cylinder

③ Assessment

In this lesson students learned to find the surface area of cylinders, square pyramids, and triangular prisms. Use the **Quick Check** problem to assess students' understanding.

Quick Check **Formative Assessment**

What is the surface area of a cylinder that is 16 cm high and has a radius of 9 cm? Round your answer to the nearest square centimeter. 1,413 cm²

Name _____

Counting Cubes to Find Volume

Materials 28 unit cubes for each student

Answer 1 to 10 to learn how to find the volume of a prism.

1. Build the rectangular prism on the right.

2. How many cubes did you use?

3. Build a second layer on the rectangular prism.

4. How many cubes did you use in the second layer? _____12_____

The **volume** of a figure is the number of cubic units needed to fill it.

A **cubic unit** is a cube with edges that are 1 unit long.

5. Find the total volume of the rectangular prism.

cubes in 1st layer	+	cubes in 2nd layer	=	total cubes
12	+	12	=	24

6. What is the total volume of the rectangular prism? _____24_____ cubic units

7. Build a third layer on the rectangular prism by putting a row of cubes on top of the back row.

8. How many cubes did you use in the third layer? _____4_____

9. Find the total volume of the figure.

cubes in 1st layer	+	cubes in 2nd layer	+	cubes in 3rd layer	=	total cubes
12	+	12	+	4	=	28

10. What is the total volume of the figure? _____28_____ cubic units

154 (student p. 1) MDIS 2.0

Name _____

Counting Cubes to Find Volume (continued)

Find the volume of each figure in cubic units.

11. _____18_____ cubic units

12. _____16_____ cubic units

13. _____18_____ cubic units

14. _____13_____ cubic units

15. _____26_____ cubic units

16. _____18_____ cubic units

17. **Reasoning** Yao made a rectangular prism with 3 layers of cubes. He put 4 cubes in each layer. What is the volume of the rectangular prism? _____12_____ cubic units

18. **Reasoning** Box A consists of 8 cubic units. Three of Box A completely fills Box B. What is the volume of Box B? _____24 cubic units_____

154 (student p. 2) MDIS 2.0

Objective Students will count cubes to find volume.
Vocabulary Volume, cubic unit
Materials 28 unit cubes for each student

❶ Conceptual Development
Use with Exercises 1–10.

In this lesson you will learn to count cubes to find volume.

Revisit the terms *volume* and *cubic unit* as needed. Have students complete Exercises 1–4. *How many cubes are in each layer?* 12 Have students complete Exercises 5–6. *Why are the cubes we are using called "unit cubes"?* They are cubes that represent one cubic unit. Have students complete Exercises 7–10.

❷ Practice Use with Exercises 11–18.

Remind students to make sure they count all the cubes, even those they cannot see. Even if a cube is not visible, it still contributes to the volume.

Error Intervention If students have difficulty counting cubes to find volume, encourage them to build the figures that are shown and count the cubes as they add them.

If You Have More Time Have students solve the following problem and explain their methods: *Luke made a shape with 31 cubes. He had 3 layers of 9 cubes completed. How many cubes will be in the top layer?* 4

❸ Assessment

In this lesson students learned to count cubes to find volume. Use the **Quick Check** problem to assess students' understanding.

Quick Check **Formative** Assessment

Ming made a shape with 5 layers of cubes. She put 7 cubes in each layer. What is the volume of her shape? 35 cubic units

MEASURING VOLUME

Name _____

Measuring Volume

Materials 28 unit cubes for each student

1. Build the rectangular prism on the right.

2. How many cubes did you use? __24__

3. What is the volume? __24__ cubic units

You can also find the volume (V) of a prism by multiplying the length (ℓ) × width (w) × height (h).

4. Find the volume if each cube is 1 cubic foot.

$V = \ell \times w \times h$

$V = \underline{4} \text{ ft} \times \underline{3} \text{ ft} \times \underline{2} \text{ ft}$

$V = \underline{24}$ cubic feet

2 ft
3 ft
4 ft
1 cube = 1 cubic foot

5. Use cubes to find the volume of the prism at the right.

$V = \underline{12}$ cubic units

6. Use multiplication to find the volume.

$V = \ell \times w \times h$

$V = \underline{2} \text{ m} \times \underline{3} \text{ m} \times \underline{2} \text{ m}$

$V = \underline{12}$ cubic meters

2 m
3 m
2 m
1 cube = 1 cubic meter

7. Find the volume of the prism at the right.

$V = \ell \times w \times h$

$V = \underline{6} \text{ in.} \times \underline{5} \text{ in.} \times \underline{10} \text{ in.}$

$V = \underline{300}$ cubic inches

10 in.
5 in.
6 in.

155 (student p. 1) MDIS 2.0

Name _____

Measuring Volume (continued)

Find the volume of each figure.

8.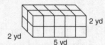
2 yd
2 yd
5 yd

__20__ cubic yards

9.
1 cube = 1 cubic centimeter

__30__ cubic centimeters

10.
4 inches

__32__ cubic inches

11.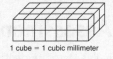
1 cube = 1 cubic millimeter

__42__ cubic millimeters

12.
3 m
3 m
3 m

__27__ m³

13.
4 in.
3 in.
8 in.

__96__ in.³

14.
7 cm
4 cm
4 cm

__112__ mm³

15.
3 yd
2 yd
2 yd

__12__ yd³

16. **Reasoning** Find the volume of a storage unit 10 feet wide, 4 feet long, and 4 feet high

__160__ cubic ft

17. **Reasoning** The volume of a rectangular prism is 12 cubic feet. The length is 6 feet and the width is 2 feet. What is the height?

__1__ foot

155 (student p. 2) MDIS 2.0

Objective Students will measure volume.
Vocabulary Volume
Materials 28 unit cubes for each student

① Conceptual Development
Use with Exercises 1–7.

In this lesson you will learn to measure volume.

Revisit the meaning of *volume.* Have students complete Exercises 1–3. *Do you think there is a way you could find the volume for something very large, such as an in-ground swimming pool?* Lead students through a discussion of multiplying length × width × height. Have students complete Exercises 4–6. *Which do you find easier: counting cubes or multiplying? Why?* Students can discuss the benefits for both ways; All answers are acceptable as long as students can validate their choice. Have students complete Exercise 7.

② Practice **Use with Exercises 8–17.**

Remind students that the formula for the volume of a rectangular prism is $V = l \times w \times h$.

Error Intervention If students have difficulty calculating volume, allow them to continue to use cubes to help them get a better understanding of the concept of volume.

If You Have More Time Have students build figures with the cubes and then have a partner find the volumes of the figures by multiplying. Have students check their multiplication by counting the cubes. Check students' work.

③ Assessment

In this lesson students learned to measure volume. Use the **Quick Check** problem to assess students' understanding.

Quick Check **Formative Assessment**

What is the volume of a cube with sides that are 12 cm each? 1,728 cubic cm

Name _____

Intervention
Lesson **156**

Comparing Volume and Surface Area

Materials 24 unit cubes for each student

Kira's dad is making her a toy box in the shape of a rectangular prism. The volume of the toy box is 24 cubic feet. He wants to know how much outside area of the box he will need to paint.

The area which needs to be painted is the surface area of the box. Find the surface area of a rectangular prism with a volume of 24 cubic feet by answering 1 to 5.

1. Use 24 cubes to make a rectangular prism like the one shown at the right. If each cube represents a cubic foot, what is the volume of the prism? **24 ft³**

2. You can find the surface area of a figure by finding the sum of the areas of each face of the figure. Complete the first row of the table for the prism you made.

Length	Width	Height	Area of Front and Back	Area of Sides	Area of Top and Bottom	Surface Area
4	3	2	16	12	24	52
6	2	2	24	8	24	56

3. If Kira's dad makes the toy box 4 feet by 3 feet by 2 feet, how much outside area of the box will he need to paint? **52** ft²

4. Use the cubes to make a different rectangular prism with a volume of 24, a width of 2, and a height of 2. Use this prism to complete the second row of the table.

5. If Kira's dad makes the toy box 6 feet by 2 feet by 2 feet, how much outside area of the box will he need to paint? **56** ft²

The area Kira's dad needs to paint depends on the dimensions he uses.

6. **Reasoning** Why is the volume of the toy box given in cubic feet and the surface area given in square feet?
Sample answer: Volume is a measure of how many cubes of a unit size can fit inside an object. Surface area is a measure of how many squares it would take to cover the outside of the object.

156 (student p. 1)   MDIS 2.0

Name _____

Intervention
Lesson **156**

Comparing Volume and Surface Area (continued)

Find the surface area and volume of each figure.

7.
SA = 22 sq. units;
V = 6 cu. units

8.
SA = 22 sq. units;
V = 6 cu. units

9.
SA = 24 sq. units;
V = 8 cu. units

10.
SA = 34 sq. units;
V = 8 cu. units

11.
SA = 42 sq. units;
V = 18 cu. units

12.
SA = 42 sq. units;
V = 18 cu. units

13.
SA = 58 sq. units;
V = 18 cu. units

14.
SA = 54 sq. units;
V = 27 cu. units

15. **Reasoning** Janet needs to determine how much wrapping paper she needs to wrap three presents of the same size. Will she need to determine the surface area or volume of the present? Explain.

Surface area; She needs to cover the surface.

156 (student p. 2)   MDIS 2.0

Objective Students will compare volume and surface area.
Vocabulary Volume, surface area, face
Materials 24 unit cubes for each student

❶ Conceptual Development
Use with Exercises 1–6.

In this lesson you will learn to compare volume and surface area.

Revisit the terms *volume, face,* and *surface area* as needed. Have students read the problem. *What do you need to find to solve this problem?* How much outside area of the box Kira's dad will need to paint, or the surface area of the box Have students complete Exercise 1. *Why is it helpful to build the shape using cubes?* I need to find the dimensions of each face. *How many faces does the box have?* 6 Have students complete Exercises 2–6.

❷ Practice Use with Exercises 7–15.

Remind students that surface area is the area of each face added together.

Error Intervention If students have difficulty differentiating between surface area and volume, try to help them remember that the surface area is just the surface, or the covering, of the outside of a shape.

If You Have More Time Have students give examples of situations in which they would need to know the volume or surface area of a shape. Check students' answers.

❸ Assessment

In this lesson students learned to compare volume and surface area. Use the **Quick Check** problem to assess students' understanding.

Quick Check **Formative Assessment**

Zack is making a cedar box in wood class. His box is 5 feet by 2 feet by 3 feet. What are the volume and surface area of his box? Volume: 30 cubic feet; surface area: 62 square feet

156   MDIS 2.0

RECORDING DATA FROM A SURVEY

Name _____

Recording Data from a Survey

Take a survey by asking, "What is your choice for a classroom mascot: a falcon, a cougar, a stingray, or a bear?" All answers will vary.

1. Write each student's answer in the box below.

Choice of Classroom Mascot

2. Make a tally mark for each choice given. Remember, tallies are made in groups of 5 so that they are easier to count.

Sample of 12 Tally Marks
‖‖ ‖‖ ‖

Choice of Classroom Mascot

Mascot	Tally	Total
Falcon		
Cougar		
Stingray		
Bear		

3. Count the tally marks. Record the total for each mascot choice.

4. How many students answered the survey? _____

5. Which mascot was chosen the most? _____

6. Which mascot was chosen the least? _____

157 (student p. 1) MDIS 2.0

Name _____

Recording Data from a Survey (continued)

Favorite Season of the Year					
Summer	Fall	Summer	Winter	Spring	Fall
Winter	Summer	Spring	Fall	Fall	Spring
Summer	Winter	Winter	Winter	Summer	Winter

7. Complete the tally chart for the data above.

Favorite Season of the Year		
Time of Year	Tally	Total
Spring	‖‖	3
Summer	‖‖‖	5
Fall	‖‖‖‖	4
Winter	‖‖‖ ‖	6

8. What was the question for the survey?

What is your favorite season of the year?

9. How many people answered the survey? 18

10. Which season was the favorite of the most people? Winter

11. Which season was the least favorite of the people? Spring

12. How many more people chose Summer over Spring? 2

13. **Reasoning** Write the seasons in order from least favorite to most favorite.

Spring, Fall, Summer, Winter

14. **Reasoning** How many more people would have to have chosen Summer for it to be the most favorite season? 2

157 (student p. 2) MDIS 2.0

Objective Students will record data from a survey.
Vocabulary Survey

① Conceptual Development
Use with Exercises 1–6.

In this lesson you will learn to record data from a survey.

Have students read the sentence at the top of the page. Do the *survey* as a class and list student choices on the board. Have students complete Exercise 1 using these responses. Have students read Exercise 2. *How can you make counting the tallies easier?* By keeping them in groups of 5, I can then skip count. Show students the sample tally marks if they are not familiar with this way of counting. Have students complete Exercises 2–6. *How many more votes were recorded for the most chosen mascot than for the least chosen mascot?* Answers will vary by class.

② Practice Use with Exercises 7–14.

Remind students that each vote is recorded by making a tally mark.

Error Intervention If students have difficulty keeping track of the votes using tally marks, encourage them to use a strip of paper to represent each vote, sort the strips into piles, and then count each pile.

If You Have More Time Have students create their own surveys and record data using tally marks. Have them write the survey question and the results on a poster. Check students' work.

③ Assessment

In this lesson students learned to record data from a survey. Use the **Quick Check** problem to assess students' understanding.

Quick Check **Formative** Assessment

How do you record 5 votes with tally marks? You draw 4 vertical tally marks and 1 tally mark diagonally across them.

Reading and Making Pictographs

Name _____

Intervention
Lesson **158**

The members of Tom's class voted for their favorite pizza toppings. The results are shown in the tally chart at the right. Answer 1 to 7 to help you make and use a pictograph of the data.

Favorite Pizza Toppings

Toppings	Tally	Number
Sausage	IIII	4
Vegetables	III	3
Pepperoni	⊬⊬⊬ ⊬⊬⊬	10

1. In the first row of the chart below write a title that best describes the pictograph. Then list the three toppings in the first column.

Favorite Pizza Toppings

Sausage	○ ○
Vegetables	○ ◖
Pepperoni	○ ○ ○ ○ ○

Each ○ = 2 votes.   Each ◖ = __1__ vote.

2. Complete the pictograph key.

3. Decide how many symbols are needed for each topping. Since sausage got 4 votes, draw 2 circles next to sausage. Since vegetables got 3 votes, draw 1 circle and 1 half-circle next to vegetables.

4. How many symbols are needed for pepperoni?   __5__

5. Draw 5 circles for pepperoni. Make sure you line up the symbols.

6. Which topping got the greatest number of votes?   __pepperoni__

7. **Reasoning** How can you tell which topping got the greatest number of votes by looking at the pictograph?

   The topping with the most number of circles got the greatest number of votes.

158 (student p. 1)   MDIS 2.0

Name _____

Intervention
Lesson **158**

Reading and Making Pictographs (continued)

For Exercises 8 to 11, use the pictograph shown at the right.

Number of Fish in the Aquarium

Silver Molly	◁▤▷ ◁▤▷ ◁▤▷ ◁▤
Black Neon Tetra	◁▤▷ ◁▤▷ ◁▤▷ ◁▤▷ ◁▤▷
Angel Fish	◁▤▷ ◁▤

Key: Each ◁▤▷ = 2 fish. Each ◁▤ = 1 fish.

8. Which fish are there the most of in the aquarium?

   __Black Neon Tetra__

9. How many Silver Molly fish are in the aquarium?   __7__

10. How many more Black Neon Tetra fish are there than Angel Fish?   __7__

11. Make a pictograph to display the data in the tally chart.

Favorite Drinks

Fruit Juice	
Lemonade	
Milk	

Key: Each 🥤 stands for _____ votes.

Favorite Drinks

Drinks	Tally	Number
Fruit Juice	⊬⊬⊬ III	8
Lemonade	⊬⊬⊬ ⊬⊬⊬ II	12
Milk	IIII	4

Sample answer: 2 votes

Use the pictograph you made in Exercise 11 to answer Exercises 12 to 15.

12. What does each 🥤 on the graph represent?   Sample answer: 2 votes

13. Which drink was chosen the least?   __milk__

14. How many more people chose lemonade over milk?   __8__

15. **Reasoning** Do any kinds of drinks on the pictograph have the same number of votes? How do you know?

   No, the graph does not have the same number of symbols for any two kinds of drinks.

158 (student p. 2)   MDIS 2.0

Objective Students will read and make pictographs.
Vocabulary Pictograph

① Conceptual Development
Use with Exercises 1–7.

In this lesson you will learn to read and make pictographs.

Review the term *pictograph* and show students some examples. Explain that in a pictograph, a picture or symbol represents a certain number of people or things. Read the problem together as a class. Have students complete Exercises 1–2. *Why did you need only one and one-half circles for vegetables?* Each circle equals 2 votes, so each half circle equals 1 vote. Have students complete Exercises 3–7. *How many circles would you need if you had 7 tally marks?* 3 whole circles and 1 half circle

② Practice Use with Exercises 8–15.

Tell students that the key shows what each symbol on the graph represents.

Error Intervention
If students have difficulty reading and making pictographs, have them practice counting by 2s, 3s, etc. Explain that students will count by the number indicated in the key and count on for half symbols.

If You Have More Time
Have students solve the following problem and explain their methods: *If you made each cup represent 4 votes, how many cups would be drawn for lemonade?* 3

③ Assessment

In this lesson students learned to read and make pictographs. Use the **Quick Check** problem to assess students' understanding.

Quick Check   Formative Assessment

Molly has a key on her pictograph that shows that 1 smiley face = 3 votes. She has 18 tallies next to peppermint. How many smiley faces will she need to draw on her pictograph for peppermint? 6

READING AND MAKING A BAR GRAPH

Reading and Making a Bar Graph

Materials colored pencils, markers, or crayons, grid paper.

Robert's class voted for their favorite country, not including the United States. The results are shown in the table.

Make and use a bar graph of the data by answering 1 to 6.

Our Favorite Countries	
Country	Votes
Canada	8
Great Britain	4
Japan	3
Mexico	11

1. Write a title above the graph. Label the axes: Country and Votes.

2. Complete the scale. Since the data go up to 11, make the scale by 2s.

3. Draw a bar for each country. Since Canada got 8 votes, color 4 squares above Canada, up to the 8 mark. For Japan, color one and a half squares because 3 is halfway between 2 and 4.

Our Favorite Countries

(bar graph: Votes on y-axis 0–12, Country on x-axis: Canada 8, Great Britain 4, Japan 3, Mexico 11)

4. Which country got the least number of votes, that is, which has the shortest bar?

   Japan

5. Which country got the greatest number of votes, that is, which has the longest bar?

   Mexico

6. **Reasoning** Which bar is twice as long as the bar for Great Britain? What does that mean?

   Canada; Twice as many students voted for Canada as voted for Great Britain.

159 (student p. 1)　　MDIS 2.0

Reading and Making a Bar Graph (continued)

Use the grid on the right for Exercises 7 to 9.

7. Draw a graph of the data in the table.

Cities We Want to See	
City	Votes
Anaheim	5
Orlando	12
Chicago	2
Washington	7

Cities We Want to See

(bar graph: Votes on y-axis 0–12, City on x-axis: Anaheim 5, Orlando 12, Chicago 2, Washington 7)

8. Which city got the most votes?

   Orlando

9. Did twice as many students vote for Orlando as voted for Washington?

   no

Use the bar graph at the right to answer Exercises 10 to 12.

10. Which craft did most students say was their favorite?

    wood carving

Favorite Crafts

(horizontal bar graph: Craft on y-axis: Boot making, Chair-caning, Rug-hooking, Wood carving; Number of People on x-axis 4, 8, 12, 16)

11. How many students chose boot making as their favorite craft demonstration?   8

12. How many more students chose wood carving than chose chair-caning as their favorite crafts?   12

159 (student p. 2)　　MDIS 2.0

Objective Students will read and make a bar graph.
Vocabulary Bar graph
Materials Colored pencils, markers, or crayons; grid paper

1 Conceptual Development
Use with Exercises 1–6.

In this lesson you will learn to read and make a bar graph.

Have students read the problem at the top of the page. *What would be a good title for the bar graph? Our Favorite Countries What is the greatest number of votes for one country?* 11 Have students complete Exercises 1–4. *Which bar is the tallest?* Mexico Have students complete Exercises 5–6.

2 Practice Use with Exercises 7–12.

Remind students to label each axis on the graphs and to look at the numbers on the axis to determine how tall to make each bar.

Error Intervention If students have difficulty reading a bar graph, suggest that they write the number represented by each bar at the end of the bar.

If You Have More Time Have students solve the following problem and explain their methods: *If twice as many students had said that rug-hooking was their favorite craft, how would the bar graph need to change?* The scale would need to go up to at least 22.

3 Assessment

In this lesson students learned to read and make a bar graph. Use the **Quick Check** problem to assess students' understanding.

Quick Check **Formative** Assessment

Draw a bar graph showing 11 singles, 4 doubles, 1 triple, and 3 home runs hit during a baseball game. Check students' work.

MAKING LINE PLOTS

Student Page 1

Name _____

Making Line Plots

A year is sometimes divided into quarters, as show at the right.

1st quarter:	January to March
2nd quarter:	April to June
3rd quarter:	July to September
4th quarter:	October to December

1. Take a survey by asking, "Which quarter of the year were you born?" Write the number of the quarter each person answers in the grid.

Quarter of the Year You Were Born

(grid)

2. What are all of the possible quarters that can be said?

   1st, 2nd, 3rd, 4th

Answer 3 to 7 to make and use a line plot of the data.

3. Draw a line. Below the line, list in order, all the possible quarters that could be said.   Line plot data will vary.

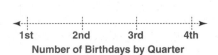

```
  1st      2nd      3rd      4th
     Number of Birthdays by Quarter
```

4. Write "Number of Birthdays by Quarter" below the line plot.

5. For each quarter that was said, mark an X above that quarter on the number line. If more than one X needs to be placed above a quarter, stack them in a single column. Answers will vary.

6. Which quarter has the most number of birthdays? _____

7. How many birthdays are after the 2nd quarter? _____

160 (student p. 1)   MDIS 2.0

Student Page 2

Name _____

Making Line Plots (continued)

The nature club leader took a survey of the number of birdfeeders each member had made during camp. The results are shown in the table.

Birdfeeders Made During Camp

Member	Made	Member	Made
Ivan	4	Luther	5
Chloe	4	Marco	5
Stacey	3	Victoria	6
Victor	6	Chi	7
Tony	5	Wesley	5
Manny	6	Wendy	5

8. Make a line plot to show the data.

```
              X
              X
        X     X
     X  X     X
  X  X  X     X     X
  3  4  5     6     7
   Number of Birdfeeders
    Made During Camp
```

9. How many members made 4 birdfeeders? __2__

10. How many members made 2 birdfeeders? __0__

11. What was the most number of birdfeeders made by a member? __7__

12. How many members made 5 or 6 birdfeeders? __8__

13. How many members made less than 6 birdfeeders? __8__

14. Did more members make more than 5 birdfeeders or less than 5 birdfeeders? __more than 5__

15. **Reasoning** By looking at the line plot, if one more person attended camp, do you think that person would probably make 4 birdfeeders or 5 birdfeeders? Explain.

    Sample answer: The person would probably make 5 birdfeeders, because the most number of people made 5 birdfeeders, and only two people made 4.

160 (student p. 2)   MDIS 2.0

Teacher Notes

Objective Students will make line plots.
Vocabulary Line plot

1 Conceptual Development
Use with Exercises 1–7.

In this lesson you will learn to make line plots.

Explain to students that a *line plot* shows information using Xs on a number line. Have students read the problem at the top of the page. Ask students to look at the months included in each quarter and find the one in which their birthday is included. Do the survey as a class, and have students record the data. Then have students complete Exercises 2–4. Demonstrate how to place an *X* for each response on the line plot. Have students complete Exercises 5–7. *Why is it helpful to see information on a line plot?* It is easy to see which category has the most, the least, and so on; it is easy to do a visual comparison.

2 Practice Use with Exercises 8–15.

Point out that an *X* on the line plot represents a nature club member, not the number of bird feeders each member made.

Error Intervention If students have difficulty making line plots, provide them with number lines and beans. Then have them use a bean instead of an X to record a response on the line plot.

If You Have More Time Have students design a survey, use it to survey their classmates, and make a line plot of the data. Check students' work.

3 Assessment

In this lesson students learned to make line plots. Use the **Quick Check** problem to assess students' understanding.

Quick Check **Formative** Assessment

Mr. Martin displays a line plot to show test scores from the social studies exam. Along the bottom are the scores from 87%–100%. The students' scores are: 87, 93, 95, 89, 83, 88, 93, 95, 87, 89, 90, and 97. Create a line plot showing these test scores. Check students' line plots.

INTERPRETING GRAPHS

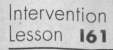

Name _____

Interpreting Graphs

Use the bar graph at the right to answer 1 to 9.

1. What is this bar graph about?
   The maximum speeds of certain animals.

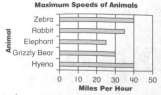

Maximum Speeds of Animals

The **scale** on a graph is the numbers used to describe the data.

2. The units used on this scale are miles per hour. What numbers does the scale use?

   0, 10, 20, 30, 40, 50

The **interval** of the scale is the number you skip count by.

3. What is the interval of the scale? __10__

4. Which animal has a maximum speed halfway between 20 and 30 miles per hour?   elephant

5. What number is halfway between 20 and 30?   25

6. What is the maximum speed of an elephant?   25 miles per hour

7. Which animal has a maximum speed of 35 miles per hour?   rabbit

8. Which animal(s) has a maximum speed that is 15 miles per hour greater than an elephant?   zebra and hyena

9. **Reasoning** Do any of the animals in the graph have a speed that is twice as fast as the elephant? How do you know?
   No; Sample answer: None of the bars are twice as long as the bar for the elephant.

Name _____

Interpreting Graphs (continued)

For 10 to 13, use the graph on the right.

Free Throw Competition

10. What is the interval of the scale for this bar graph?   2

11. Which student made the most free throws?   Janet

12. How many free throws did Tawny make?   7

13. How many more free throws did Janet make than Ian?   5

For 14 to 18, use the graph on the right.

National Park Visitation Poll

14. What is the interval of the scale?   50

15. Which park received 275 votes?   Mammoth Cave

16. Which park received twice as many votes as Carlsbad Caverns?   Yellowstone

17. How many fewer votes did Carlsbad Caverns receive than the Grand Canyon?   200

18. **Reasoning** Which two parks received the closest number of votes? Explain how you know.
    Sample answer: Mammoth Cave and Yellowstone; These are the two that have bars that are closest in length. That makes them closest in number of votes.

Objective Students will interpret graphs.
Vocabulary Bar graph, scale, interval

① Conceptual Development
Use with Exercises 1–9.

In this lesson you will learn to interpret graphs.

Revisit the term *bar graph*. Have students identify the title of the bar graph to complete Exercise 1. Have students point out the *scale* on the bar graph and the *interval* of the scale—the jump between the numbers—and then complete Exercise 2–9. *How does understanding the scale of the graph help you to know when a bar is between two numbers?* If I didn't know that there were 10 miles between each number on the scale, I would not be able to understand that the number represented by a bar midway between two numbers is 5 more miles per hour.

② Practice Use with Exercises 10–18.

Remind students to check their understanding of the scale for each graph before they try to interpret the information given.

Error Intervention If students have difficulty interpreting the graphs, help them to refresh their skip-counting skills or give them a chart with skip counting so they can see how to read the data shown.

If You Have More Time Have students solve the following problem and explain their methods: *Why are scaled intervals sometimes vitally important to creating a bar graph?* When the numbers that represent the data are so great, there has to be a condensed way to show them on a graph to avoid the graph from being larger than the paper could physically accommodate.

③ Assessment

In this lesson students learned to interpret graphs. Use the **Quick Check** problem to assess students' understanding.

Quick Check **Formative Assessment**

You are making a bar graph to describe the following situation: If Tobe climbed 250 stairs, what could be the scale of the bar graph? Accept all reasonable answers. Sample answer: The scale would be every 50 steps.

Stem-and-Leaf Plots

The number of points earned on a history project, by each of nine students, are:

12, 27, 10, 18, 29, 12, 23, 12, 19

Answer 1 to 12, to make and use a stem-and-leaf plot of the data.

Make the **stem** the first digit of each number.

Points Earned	
Stem	**Leaves**
1	0 2 2 2 8 9
2	3 7 9

1 | 8 = 18

1. What two stems are found in the data? _1 and 2_

2. Write the stems, 1 and 2, in order from least to greatest under the heading Stem.

3. List all the numbers that have 1 as a stem.   12, 10, 18, 12, 12, 19

4. Write the numbers that have 1 as a stem in order from least to greatest.   10, 12, 12, 12, 18, 19

5. List all the numbers that have 2 as a stem.   27, 29, 23

6. Write the numbers that have 2 as a stem in order from least to greatest.   23, 27, 29

Make the **leaf** the second digit of each number. The leaves are listed in order from least to greatest after each stem.

7. Since 10 is the least number with a stem of 1, write a 0 after the stem 1. Since 12 is next, write 2 after the 0. Write the remaining leaves after the stem 1.

8. Since 23 is the least number with a stem of 2, write a 3 after the stem 2. Put this directly below the 0. Put 7 below the first leaf of 2 for 27 and 9 below the second 2.

9. What is the mode of the points earned data? _12_

162 (student p. 1)   MDIS 2.0

Stem-and-Leaf Plots (continued)

10. What is the median of the points earned data? _18_

11. What is the range of the points earned data? _19_

12. What is the mean of the points earned data? _18_

For Exercises 13 to 17 make a stem-and-leaf plot and then answer the questions. For one-digit numbers, use a zero in the stem.

13. Organize the data below for the pounds of newspapers collected by the classes for recycling into a stem-and-leaf plot:
6, 18, 12, 13, 11, 12, 12

14. Find the mean of the data. _12_

15. Find the range of the data. _12_

16. Find the median of the data. _12_

17. Find the mode(s) of the data. _12_

Stem	Leaves
0	6
1	1 2 2 2 3 8

Use the stem-and-leaf plot on the right for Exercises 18 to 22.

18. What is the mode(s)? _35 and 38_

19. What is the median? _35_

20. What is the range? _17_

21. What is the mean? _33_

Length in Miles	
Stem	**Leaves**
2	2 4
3	5 5 8 8 9

22. **Reasoning** How would the recycling stem-and-leaf plot from Exercise 13 change if the class that collected 6 pounds had collected 26 pounds?

Sample answer: There would not be a 0 stem with a 6 for the leaf, instead there would be a 2 stem with a 6 for the leaf. The 2 stem would be written below the 1 stem.

162 (student p. 2)   MDIS 2.0

Objective Students will create and use a stem-and-leaf plot.

Vocabulary Mode, median, range, mean, stem, leaf

❶ Conceptual Development
Use with Exercises 1–12.

In this lesson you will learn to make and use a stem-and-leaf plot.

Revisit the terms *mode*, *median*, *range*, and *mean* as needed. Point out that the *stem* of each number in the data set is the first digit, and the *leaf* is the second digit. In this data set, the stems are the tens and the leaves are the ones. Draw attention to the key, which tells how the stems and leaves are divided in the plot. Have students complete Exercises 1–12. *Why do you think it is necessary to put the stem-and-leaf numbers in order from least to greatest?* All the data needs to be in order because the stems and leaves will be used to create in the stem-and-leaf plot the other numbers that were found. Maintaining an order makes it easier to read the stem-and-leaf plot.

❷ Practice Use with Exercises 13–22.

Remind students to first look at all of the numbers to find the least stem and then list stems in order from least to greatest down the column.

Error Intervention If students have difficulty making or using stem-and-leaf plots, encourage them to think of the numbers in terms of tens and ones.

If You Have More Time Have students use real data, such as the ages of people in their family or class, to construct a stem-and-leaf plot.

❸ Assessment

In this lesson students learned to make and use a stem-and-leaf plot. Use the **Quick Check** problem to assess students' understanding.

Quick Check **Formative** Assessment

Organize the data for the points scored per game into a stem-and-leaf plot: 34, 49, 39, 29, 41, 43, 31. Find the mean, median, mode, and range of the data. Check students' stem-and-leaf plots.; 38; 39; no mode; 20

HISTOGRAMS

Histograms

Materials colored pencils

A **histogram** is a bar graph that has no space between the bars.
A histogram has equal intervals on the horizontal axis.

The table shows the ages of 25 people who attended a play. Complete the histogram based on the data given in the table by answering 1 to 9.

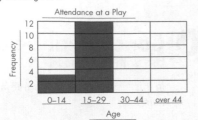

Age	Frequency
0–14	3
15–29	12
30–44	5
over 44	5

1. List the age intervals in each blank along the horizontal axis.

2. Label the scale along the vertical axis. Make each interval the same.

3. Give the graph a title and label the axes.

4. How many people were 14 and under? _____ 3

5. Color a bar of height 3 above 0–14.

6. How many people were 15 to 29? Color a bar that height above 15–29. _____ 12

7. How many people were 30 to 44? Color a bar that height above 30–44. _____ 5

8. How many people were over 44? Color a bar that height above "over 44." _____ 5

9. Did more people between the ages of 15 and 29 attend the play than people over 29? _____ yes

Copyright © Pearson Education, Inc., or its affiliates. All Rights Reserved. **163** (student p. 1) MDIS 2.0

Histograms (continued)

The histogram shows the time, in minutes, that people who were surveyed spend driving to work. Use the graph for Exercises 10 to 13.

10. How many people were surveyed? _____ 100

11. How much time did 20% of the people surveyed spend driving to work? _____ 60–79 minutes

12. How much time did the most people spend driving to work? _____ 40–59 minutes

13. **Reasoning** Did twice as many of the people surveyed spend 40 to 59 minutes driving to work as spend 20 to 39 minutes? Explain how you can tell from the graph.

Yes; the bar for 40–59 is twice as high as the bar for 20–39.

14. The table shows the results of a survey on the age of people visiting a restaurant. Use the data to complete the histogram.

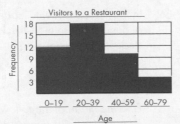

Age	Frequency
0–19	12
20–39	18
40–59	10
60–79	4

Copyright © Pearson Education, Inc., or its affiliates. All Rights Reserved. **163** (student p. 2) MDIS 2.0

Objective Students will create histograms.
Vocabulary Histogram
Materials Colored pencils

1 Conceptual Development
Use with Exercises 1–9.

In this lesson you will learn to create and use a histogram.

Show students that the data for the first column of the table will be listed along the horizontal axis. Then guide students to decide on a scale to use for the vertical axis. *Why would a scale of 2, 4, 6, 8, 10, and 12 be a good choice?* The highest frequency is 12. Have students complete Exercises 1–9. *Does a histogram remind you of another type of graph?* Histograms are similar to bar graphs, but histograms do not have space between the bars.

2 Practice Use with Exercises 10–14.

Remind students to look at both axes of the histogram to be sure they understand what the histogram represents.

Error Intervention If students have difficulty with creating and interpreting a histogram, provide them with a piece of construction paper and linking cubes and allow them to use these to represent the data before transferring the data to their paper.

If You Have More Time Have students find out how many minutes each of their classmates spends doing some activity, such as playing video games, traveling to school, or practicing a musical instrument. Have them construct a histogram for their data.

3 Assessment

In this lesson students learned to create and use a histogram. Use the **Quick Check** problem to assess students' understanding.

Quick Check Formative Assessment

Students gathered data about the number of pairs of shoes they owned: 11 owned 1–3 pairs, 4 owned 4–6 pairs, 0 owned 7–9 pairs, and 3 owned 10–12 pairs. Which group will not have a bar colored on the histogram? The group owning 7–9 pairs of shoes

Name _____

Finding the Mean

Materials color tiles: 5 red, 12 blue, and 7 yellow for each
student or group

The **mean,** or average, is the sum of all the numbers in a set of
data divided by the total number of data.

Carlos made 5 baskets in his first basketball game of the season,
12 baskets in the second game, and 7 in the third game.
What is the mean number of baskets that Carlos made during
the first three games?

Find the mean by answering 1 to 3.

1. Use tiles to represent the number of baskets that Carlos made. Make one
stack of 5 red tiles to represent the baskets in the first game, one stack of
12 blue tiles to represent the baskets in the second game and one stack of
7 yellow tiles to represent baskets in the third game.

2. Move tiles from one stack to another until there are three
stacks of equal height.

3. How many tiles are in each stack?   ___8___
This number represents the average number of baskets
in each game or the mean.

Find the mean without using tiles by answering 4 to 6.

4. What is the total number of baskets that Carlos
made in all three games? $5 + 12 + 7 =$ ___24___

5. If 24 tiles are divided between three stacks,
how many tiles are in each stack? $24 \div 3 =$ ___8___

6. Because there were 3 games, the total number of baskets
was divided by 3. This is the mean. Is this number the
same as the mean found when using the tiles?   ___yes___

7. **Reasoning** Carlos scored no points in the fourth game of
the season. What effect does that have on the mean?
The mean would decrease. It would be 6 rather than 8.

164 (student p. 1)   MDIS 2.0

Name _____

Finding the Mean (continued)

Find the mean for each data set.

8. $120, $280, $410, $300, $180
$258

9. 175 ft, 136 ft, 157 ft, 112 ft
145 ft

10. 23 in., 37 in., 67 in., 93 in., 25 in.
49 in.

11. 5,341 km, 6,780 km, 2,543 km
4,888 km

12. 89 weeks, 37 weeks, 27 weeks,
12 weeks, 86 weeks, 97 weeks
58 weeks

13. 3 runs, 5 runs, 8 runs, 4 runs,
10 runs, 5 runs, 4 runs, 1 run
5 runs

14. $991, $759, $610, $967, $733
$812

15. 36 lb, 53 lb, 25 lb, 14 lb
32 lb

16. 76 bulbs, 36 bulbs, 98 bulbs,
25 bulbs, 38 bulbs, 27 bulbs
50 bulbs

17. 1,664 books, 2,533 books,
1,267 books, 7,668 books
3,283 books

18. $67, $44, $32, $86, $12, $11
$42

19. 379 points, 255 points, 116 points
250 points

20. $1,561; $2,689; $1,442;
$3,522; $1,756
$2,194

21. 4 h, 1 h, 0 h, 5 h, 7 h,
0 h, 5 h, 2 h
3 h

22. Dale worked 7 days and made $350. What was the
average amount he made each day? $50 each day

23. **Reasoning** Mrs. Hernandez's math class made the
following scores on a quiz: 5, 7, 8, 7, 9, 10, 2, 2, 3.
If 2 points are added to everybody's score, how is the
mean affected?
The mean is raised by 2.

164 (student p. 2)   MDIS 2.0

Objective Students will find the mean of a set of
numbers.
Vocabulary Mean
Materials Color tiles: 5 red, 12 blue, and 7 yellow
for each student or group

① Conceptual Development
Use with Exercises 1–7.

*In this lesson you will learn to find the mean of a set of
numbers.*

Remind students that the *mean* is the same as the
average of a set of numbers. Have students work in
pairs to complete Exercises 1–7. *How did using tiles
help you to find the mean of the number of baskets
Carlos made?* Using tiles allowed me to see how the
mean is an average of all the numbers combined. If you
knew that the average number of baskets in each game
was 8, and that three games were played, how could
you find the total number of baskets made? Sample
answer: I could take the average number of baskets
made, 8, and multiply that number by the number of
games played, 3. $8 \times 3 = 24$, so the total number of
points that Carlos scored in the three games is 24 points.

② Practice Use with Exercises 8–23.

Remind students that to find the mean, you add all
of the numbers in the set and then divide by the total
number of numbers.

Error Intervention If students have difficulty
finding the mean, allow them to continue to use the
color tiles and break the numbers into equal groups.

If You Have More Time Have students
respond to the following: How does adding a zero to
any data set change the mean? Even though it does
not change the total, it does change the number you
need to divide by, which will lower the mean.

③ Assessment

In this lesson students learned to find the mean of a set
of numbers. Use the **Quick Check** problem to assess
students' understanding.

Quick Check **Formative**
Assessment

*Find the mean of the following set of data: 780 guests,
816 guests, 699 guests, 857 guests, 893 guests.*
809 guests; $780 + 816 + 699 + 857 + 893 = 4,045$;
$4,045 \div 5 = 809$

---

164   MDIS 2.0

MEDIAN, MODE, AND RANGE

Name _____

Median, Mode, and Range

Materials 40-50 color tiles, counters or other small object placed in a clear container

How many items are in the container? Collect your classmates' guesses and find the median, mode, and range of the data by answering 1 to 7.

1. Ask 9 people in your class to guess the number of items in the container. Write the 9 guesses in the blanks below. These numbers are the data.
Answers will vary.

_____

The **median** is the middle number when the data are listed in order.

2. List the data in order from least to greatest. If there are some data that are the same, list those multiple times.
Answers will vary. Numbers should be least to greatest.

_____

3. Circle the number that is in the middle of the list.
What is the median of your data? _____ Check work.

The **mode** is the data value that occurs most often. If there is more than one number that appears the most often, it is possible to have more than one mode. If each number appears only once, then there is no mode.

4. How many modes are there for your data? _____ Check work.

5. What is the mode of your data? _____ Check work.

The **range** is the difference between the greatest and least data values.

6. What is the difference between the greatest and the least data values? _____ Check work.

7. Count the number of items in the container. Was the median, mode, or range closest to the actual number of items? _____ Check work.

165 (student p. 1)   MDIS 2.0

Name _____

Median, Mode, and Range (continued)

Find the median, mode and range of each data set.

8. 2, 5, 1, 8, 8, 12, 6
median ___6___
mode(s) ___8___
range ___11___

9. 25, 60, 20, 45, 25
median ___25___
mode(s) ___25___
range ___40___

10. 54, 54, 60
median ___54___
mode(s) ___54___
range ___6___

11. 4, 1, 1, 8, 8, 12, 8
median ___8___
mode(s) ___8___
range ___11___

12. 35, 23, 15, 23, 24
median ___23___
mode(s) ___23___
range ___20___

13. 15, 11, 12, 18, 14, 11, 9, 14, 13
median ___13___
mode(s) ___11,14___
range ___9___

14. If the number 8 were removed from the data in Exercise 11, what two numbers would be in the middle of the data? ___4 and 8___

The average, or mean, of 4 and 8 is the median. What is the median of the data after removing the number 8? ___6___

15. **Reasoning** If the number 100 is added to the data in Exercise 12, how does that affect the mean, median, mode, and range?
The mean would be quite a bit higher. The median and mode would be the same. The range would be much larger.

16. Brandi's scores on math exams were as follows: 96, 96, 89, 84, 25. Find the mean, median, and mode for Brandi's quiz scores.
The mean is 78, the median is 89, and the mode is 96.

17. **Reasoning** Which of the measures that you found in Exercise 16 best represents a typical exam score for Brandi? Explain.
The median is more typical. The mode is too high and the mean is too low.

165 (student p. 2)   MDIS 2.0

Objective Students will find the median, mode, and range of a set of numbers.
Vocabulary Median, mode, range
Materials 40–50 color tiles, counters, or other small objects placed in a clear container

❶ Conceptual Development
Use with Exercises 1–7.

In this lesson you will learn to find the median, mode, and range of a set of numbers.

Revisit the terms *median, mode,* and *range.* Have students complete Exercises 1–3. *Why is it important to have your numbers in order from least to greatest when finding the median?* The median is the middle number, so if the numbers are not listed in order, the middle number won't be in the middle position. Have students complete Exercises 4–5. *What would the mode be if all numbers occurred only once?* There would be no mode.

❷ Practice Use with Exercises 8–17.

Remind students that the median is the middle number when the numbers are listed in order, the mode is the number that occurs most often, and the range is the difference between the greatest number and the least number.

Error Intervention If students have difficulty remembering the meaning of median, mode, and range, provide them with simple clues, such as: Median is like the median in the road—in the middle.

If You Have More Time Generate real data by timing how long it takes students to complete a simple task, such as transferring marbles from one cup to another or sorting a mixture of different-colored beads. Have students find the median, mode, range, and mean of the class's data.

❸ Assessment

In this lesson students learned to find the median, mode, and range of a set of numbers. Use the **Quick Check** problem to assess students' understanding.

Quick Check **Formative** Assessment

Find the median, mode, and range of the following data set: $14, $13, $17, $12, $13, $19, $20.
Median: $14, mode: $13, range: $8

MDIS 2.0

Name ______________________

Scatterplots

Intervention Lesson **166**

Amishi often sits in the park and counts butterflies. She makes a note of the number of minutes she sits outside and the number of butterflies she sees.

The table to the right shows the data she has collected.

Number of Minutes	Number of Butterflies
2	1
5	3
8	4
17	8
25	12
29	17

Use this information to answer 1 through 7.

1. How would you label the axes for a scatterplot of this data?

x-axis: Number of Minutes
y-axis: Number of Butterflies

2. What is a reasonable scale and interval for the *x*-axis? Explain.
Sample answer: The number of minutes ranges from 2 to 29, so I would use a scale from 0 to 30 with intervals of 5.

3. What is a reasonable scale and interval for the *y*-axis? Explain.
Sample answer: The number of butterflies ranges from 1 to 17, so I would use a scale from 0 to 20 with intervals of 5.

4. What would be a good title for the scatterplot?
Sample answer: Butterflies Amishi Saw at the Park

5. Explain how to plot the points on the scatterplot.
Sample answer: Each row of the table is an ordered pair. The number in the first column is the *x*-value. The number in the second column is the *y*-value.

6. Name two ordered pairs from the table.
Sample answer: (2, 1) and (17, 8)

7. Make a scatterplot of the data in the table.

Name ______________________

Scatterplots (continued)

Intervention Lesson **166**

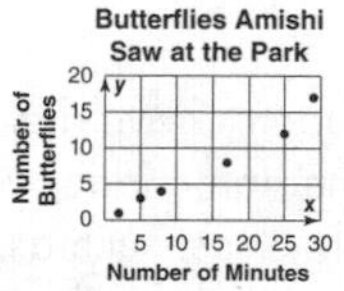

Use the scatterplot above to answer 8 through 13.

8. What is the trend shown in the scatterplot?
As the number of minutes increases, the number of butterflies seen increases.

9. What does the point (8, 4) represent?
When Amishi sat outside for 8 minutes, she saw 4 butterflies.

10. How many butterflies did Amishi see when she sat outside for 25 minutes?
12

11. About how many more butterflies did she see in 29 minutes than she saw in 5 minutes?
Sample answer: About 15

12. About how many butterflies do you think Amishi would see if she sat outside for 22 minutes?
Sample answer: About 10

13. About how many butterflies do you think Amishi would see if she sat outside for 40 minutes?
Sample answer: About 22

Objective Students will make a scatterplot and solve problems using a scatterplot.
Vocabulary scatterplot, trend, discrete data

1 Conceptual Development

Use with Exercises 1–7.

In this lesson you will learn to make a scatterplot and solve problems using a scatterplot.

Have students read the scenario and table at the top of the page. Revisit the terms *scatterplot, trend,* and *discrete data* as needed. Have students complete Exercise 1. *What information is shown in the first column of the table?* The number of minutes *What information is shown in the second column of the table?* The number of butterflies *How do you determine the scale for an axis?* Sample answer: Look at the lowest value and highest value and choose a scale that includes all of the values Have students complete Exercises 2–7.

2 Practice Use with Exercises 8–13.

Explain that a trend in a scatterplot is the relationship between the two sets of values. In this situation, the trend is the relationship between the number of minutes and the number of butterflies seen.

Error Intervention If students have difficulty predicting the number of butterflies Amishi would see in 40 minutes, encourage them to draw a straight line that is close to most of the data points on the scatterplot. Then have them extend the line to 40 minutes.

If You Have More Time Have students solve the following problem and explain their methods: *Name a real-world situation that would show a trend in which one set of values decreases as the other increases. Also name a situation in which there is no relationship between the sets of values.* Answers will vary. Check to ensure that students' responses meet the specified criteria.

3 Assessment

In this lesson students learned to make a scatterplot and solve problems using a scatterplot. Use the **Quick Check** problem to assess students' understanding.

Quick Check Formative Assessment

What are two types of questions you can answer by looking at a scatterplot? Sample answer: You can see the trend in the data. Also, you can predict what a value will be.

MEASURING CAPACITY OR WEIGHT

Name _____

Measuring Capacity or Weight

Jenna is going camping. She wants to bring a large pitcher so that she can make lemonade at the campsite.

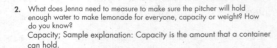

She wants to make sure that the pitcher is not too heavy because she needs to carry it on the long walk to the campsite. And she needs to make sure it holds enough water to make lemonade for everyone.

Use this information to answer 1 through 6.

1. What does Jenna need to measure to make sure the pitcher is not too heavy to carry on the long walk, capacity or weight? How do you know?
   Weight; Sample explanation: The weight of an object is how heavy it is.

2. What does Jenna need to measure to make sure the pitcher will hold enough water to make lemonade for everyone, capacity or weight? How do you know?
   Capacity; Sample explanation: Capacity is the amount that a container can hold.

3. What unit might Jenna use to measure the weight of the pitcher?
   Sample answer: Pounds

4. What are two different units that Jenna might use to measure the capacity of the pitcher?
   Sample answer: Gallons or cups

5. Karen carried a tent to the campsite. Jenna was curious to know how heavy the tent was, so Karen told her the weight. What units did Karen most likely use—ounces, pounds, or tons? Explain.
   Pounds; Sample explanation: Ounces are used to measure the weight of a very light object, such as a pencil or mouse. Tons are used to measure the weight of a very heavy object, such as a truck or whale.

6. Jenna's friend Raud drove his truck to the campsite. The roof rack on the truck can safely hold up to 125 pounds. Raud wants to know whether he can carry a canoe on the roof rack. To decide, does he need to know the capacity or weight of the canoe? Explain.
   Weight; Sample explanation: The weight of an object is how heavy it is, and the roof rack has a weight limit of 125 pounds.

167 (student p. 1)   MDIS 2.0

Name _____

Measuring Capacity or Weight (continued)

In 7 through 14, circle the correct answer.

7. Jack is making 3 quarts of chili. He wants to make sure that the pot he is using is large enough. Which is important for Jack to know?
   (The capacity of the pot)   The weight of the pot

8. Maria drinks 8 glasses of water a day. She wants to know how much water she is actually drinking. Which should she measure?
   (The capacity of the glass)   The weight of the glass

9. Gustav is filling a box with glass vases. He wants to make sure he can carry the box after it has been filled. What does Gustav need to know about each vase?
   The capacity of each vase   (The weight of each vase)

10. Mr. Brook's class is doing a science experiment. They are using ounces as the measurement unit. What are they measuring?
    Capacity   (Weight)

11. Kayla bought a 12-ounce bag of nuts. What does she know about the bag?
    The capacity of the bag   (The weight of the bag)

12. Damian bought a sandbox for his children. He knows how much sand the sandbox can hold. What does he know about the sandbox?
    (The capacity of the sandbox)   The weight of the sandbox

13. Juanita pours a quart of milk into a bowl and sees that the bowl is only half full. What is she measuring?
    (The capacity of the bowl)   The weight of the bowl

14. Which unit would you use to measure the weight of a stack of pennies?
    Pints   (Ounces)

167 (student p. 2)   MDIS 2.0

Objective Students will determine whether to measure capacity or weight.
Vocabulary Capacity, weight

① Conceptual Development
Use with Exercises 1–6.

In this lesson you will learn to determine whether to measure capacity or weight.

Have students read the scenario at the top of the page. Revisit the terms *capacity* and *weight* as needed. Have students complete Exercise 1. *What does Jenna need to find out about the pitcher?* She wants to make sure it isn't too heavy. *Is the capacity or weight of an object how heavy it is?* Weight *What is capacity?* How much something can hold Have students complete Exercises 2–6.

② Practice Use with Exercises 7–14.

Explain that an object can have both capacity and weight. The capacity of an object is the amount that it can hold. The weight of an object is how heavy it is.

Error Intervention If students have difficulty identifying which units to use in different situations, encourage them to make a table. Have them list units for capacity and units for weight. Next to each unit, have them write an example of something they could measure using that unit.

If You Have More Time Have students solve the following problem: *Calvin is shopping for a large ceramic planter for his balcony. Why might it be important for him to know both the weight and the capacity of the planter?* Sample answer: He would need to know the weight of the planter to make sure that the balcony is strong enough to hold it. He would need to know the capacity so he knows how much soil he can put in the planter.

③ Assessment

In this lesson students learned to determine whether to measure capacity or weight. Use the **Quick Check** problem to assess students' understanding.

Quick Check **Formative Assessment**

Jo is looking for a serving bowl for a party. The bowl must be able to hold at least 2 gallons of punch. What does she need to know about a serving bowl to know whether it will work, the capacity or weight? Capacity

---

Name _____

Intervention
Lesson **168**

Solving Problems with Units of Time

Several friends signed up together for a creative writing class. This week's assignment is shown to the right.

Use this information to answer 1 through 4.

Creative Writing Class Weekly Assignment	
Write in your journal	40 minutes
Write a poem	15 minutes
Read short stories	25 minutes

1. Mariano has read a short story for 8 minutes. How much longer does he need to read? Show how to use a bar diagram to find the answer.
   <u>17 minutes</u>

   Sample bar diagram given

   | 8 | ? |

2. Alana has finished writing in her journal and writing a poem. How much time has she spent on her assignment? Show how to use a number line to find the answer.
   <u>55 minutes</u>

   Sample number line given

3. Harrison wrote in his journal for 12 minutes in the morning. After lunch, he read short stories for 17 minutes. How many minutes has he worked on his assignments? Show how to use both a bar diagram and a number line to find the answer.
   <u>29 minutes</u>

   Sample number line and bar diagram given
   | 12 | 17 |

4. Olivia only has 9 more minutes of journal writing to do. How many minutes has she already spent writing in her journal? Show how to use a bar diagram to find the answer.
   <u>31 minutes</u>

   40 minutes
   | ? | 9 |
   Sample bar diagram given

168 (student p. 1)   MDIS 2.0

Name _____

Intervention
Lesson **168**

Solving Problems with Units of Time (continued)

For 5 through 13, solve each problem. You may use a bar diagram or number line to help you.

5. Tom tutors one student in math for 15 minutes. He tutors another student in science for 22 minutes. How long does he spend tutoring?
   <u>37 minutes</u>

6. The drive from Lowell to Norton is 55 minutes. Ruth has already driven 42 minutes. How many more minutes does she have to drive?
   <u>13 minutes</u>

7. Jada spends 18 minutes planting flowers in her garden. Then she takes a walk around the neighborhood for 23 minutes. Later that day, she plays tennis at the park for 15 minutes. How much time does she spend outdoors?
   <u>56 minutes</u>

8. Lisa napped for 37 minutes. Her sister Jody napped for 8 fewer minutes than Lisa. For how many minutes did Jody nap?
   <u>29 minutes</u>

9. Joy watches two cartoons. Each cartoon is 18 minutes long. How long does she watch cartoons?
   <u>36 minutes</u>

10. Gary walks for 35 minutes every day. He only has 11 more minutes to walk today. For how many minutes has he already walked?
    <u>24 minutes</u>

11. Cassie spends 45 minutes running three errands. It takes her 12 minutes to go to the post office. It takes her another 17 minutes to go to the grocery store. How long did it take her to run her third errand?
    <u>16 minutes</u>

12. Art class is 52 minutes long. Class began 19 minutes ago. How many more minutes does art class last?
    <u>33 minutes</u>

13. Molly is playing math games on the computer. She plays one math game for 28 minutes, and she plays another math game for 29 minutes. How many minutes does Molly play math games on the computer?
    <u>57 minutes</u>

168 (student p. 2)   MDIS 2.0

Objective Students will add and subtract time intervals.

Vocabulary Time interval

① Conceptual Development
Use with Exercises 1–4.

In this lesson you will learn to add and subtract time intervals.

Have students read the scenario at the top of the page. Revisit the term *time interval* as needed. Have students complete Exercise 1. *How much time has Mariano spent reading a short story?* 8 minutes *How much time does he need to spend reading short stories in all?* 25 minutes *What does the strip diagram show?* 8 *plus what number is 25?* Have students complete Exercises 2–4.

② Practice **Use with Exercises 5–13.**

Explain that students will be adding and subtracting to solve these problems. If students need to find the total amount of time, they should add. If they need to find the amount of time that is left, they should subtract.

Error Intervention If students have difficulty solving any of the problems, encourage them to draw a strip diagram or a number line. For example, for Exercise 11, they can draw a strip diagram that shows that 12 plus 17 plus some number is 45.

If You Have More Time Have students solve the following problem and explain their methods: *Eliot trained for baseball season by running the bases for 20 minutes. He spent 5 more minutes taking batting practice than he spent running the bases. He spent 10 more minutes catching fly balls than he spent taking batting practice. How much time did he spend training in all?* $20 + 25 + 35 = 80$ minutes

③ Assessment

In this lesson students learned to add and subtract time intervals. Use the **Quick Check** problem to assess students' understanding.

Quick Check **Formative** Assessment

Julia spent 52 minutes cleaning her house. She spent 17 minutes cleaning the kitchen. How much time did she spend cleaning the rest of the house? 35 minutes

---

Name _____

Intervention Lesson **169**

Making Dot Plots

Adella invited 22 friends to her birthday party. The table shows the ages of her friends at the party.

Use this information to answer 1 through 7.

Adella's Birthday Party	
Age	Number of Friends
8	4
9	8
10	6
11	3
12	1

1. What is a reasonable scale for a dot plot of the data in the table? How do you know?
   Sample answer: From 7 to 13; This scale includes all of the data.

2. What would be a good title for the dot plot?
   Sample answer: Friends at Adella's Birthday Party

3. How can you make a dot plot of the data in the table?
   Sample answer: After you choose a scale for the number line, draw one dot above each age for each friend with that age.

4. Make a dot plot for the data in the table.

   Friends at Adella's Birthday Party

   7 8 9 10 11 12 13

5. What is the age of the youngest friend at the party? ___8___

6. What is the age of the oldest friend at the party? ___12___

7. What is the most common age at Adella's party? ___9___

Name _____

Intervention Lesson **169**

Making Dot Plots (continued)

Ms. Gold's English class had a contest to see how many books students could read over the summer. 1 student read 2 books. 5 students read 4 books. 9 students read 5 books. 6 students read 6 books. 3 students read 7 books. 2 students read 9 books.

Use this information to answer 8 through 15.

8. What is a reasonable scale for a dot plot of this data?
   Sample answer: 1 to 10

9. Make a dot plot for the data.

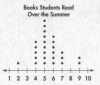

   Books Students Read Over the Summer

   1 2 3 4 5 6 7 8 9 10

10. How many students read 4 books? ___5___

11. How many students read 8 books? ___None___

12. What was the most common number of books read? ___5___

13. What was the least number of books read by a student? ___2___

14. What was the greatest number of books read by a student? ___9___

15. How many students read 7 or more books? ___5___

Objective Students will make dot plots and solve problems using dot plots.
Vocabulary dot plot

1 Conceptual Development
Use with Exercises 1–7.

In this lesson you will learn to make dot plots and solve problems using dot plots.

Have students read the scenario and table at the top of the page. Revisit the term *dot plot* as needed. Have students complete Exercise 1. *How old is the youngest friend at the party?* 8 *How old is the oldest friend at the party?* 12 *How many dots should you draw above 10 on the number line?* 6 Have students complete Exercises 2–7.

2 Practice **Use with Exercises 8–15.**

Explain that dot plots help you analyze data by viewing it graphically. For example, you can find the number of books that occurs most often by looking for the tallest stack of dots.

Error Intervention If students have difficulty answering Exercise 11, point out that a number on the number line might have no data. If there is no dot above a number on the number line, there is no data for that number. For example, there may be no 13-year-olds at a party, or, in this case, no students read 8 books.

If You Have More Time Have students use the dot plot in Exercise 9 to solve the following problem and explain their methods: *Did more students read fewer than 5 books or more than 6 books?* Fewer than 5 books

3 Assessment

In this lesson students learned to make dot plots and solve problems using dot plots. Use the **Quick Check** problem to assess students' understanding.

Quick Check **Formative Assessment**

Nadia received the following scores on 10 quizzes: 18, 15, 20, 18, 16, 18, 19, 15, 18, and 17. If you made a dot plot of this data, what would be the most common test score? 18

CONVERTING UNITS

Student Page 1

Converting Units

Mandy brought 1.75 gallons of lemonade to the picnic.
Answer the following to find how many one-cup servings
she can make.

1. It takes 16 cups to equal a gallon. Complete the conversion factor.
   $\dfrac{\boxed{16}\ c}{\boxed{1}\ g}$

2. Write an equivalent rate.
   $\dfrac{\boxed{16}\ c \times 1.75}{\boxed{1}\ g \times 1.75} = \dfrac{\boxed{28}\ c}{1.75\ g}$

3. Mandy can make __28__ one-cup servings.

Juan brought a 6-pack of juice bottles to the picnic.
Each bottle holds 10 fluid ounces of juice. Answer the
following to find how many one-cup servings he can make.

4. Juan brought __60__ fluid ounces of juice in all.

5. It takes 8 fluid ounces to equal a cup. To write
   an equivalent rate like the one at the right, think:
   What times 8 equals 60? Solve $8n = 60$.

   $\dfrac{1\ c}{8\ fl\ oz} = \dfrac{\boxed{}\ c}{60\ fl\ oz}$

   $8n = 60$

   $\dfrac{8n}{8} = \dfrac{60}{8}$

   $n = \underline{7.5}$

6. Write an equivalent rate.
   $\dfrac{1\ c \times \boxed{7.5}}{8\ fl\ oz \times \boxed{7.5}} = \dfrac{\boxed{7.5}\ c}{60\ fl\ oz}$

7. Juan can make __7.5__ one-cup servings.

170 (student p. 1)   MDIS 2.0

Student Page 2

Converting Units (continued)

George brought 2.25 pounds of hamburger to the
picnic. Answer the following to find how many
four-ounce servings he can make.

8. It takes 16 ounces to equal a pound. Use
   dimensional analysis to find how many
   ounces are in 2.25 lb.

   $\boxed{2.25}\ lb \times \dfrac{\boxed{16}\ oz}{1\ lb} = \boxed{2.25} \times \boxed{16}\ oz = \boxed{36}\ oz$ $2.25\ lb = \underline{36}\ oz$

9. George can make __9__ four-ounce servings.

Kara brought a 42-inch long sandwich to the picnic.
Answer the following to find how many feet long the
sandwich is.

10. It takes 12 inches to equal a foot. Use dimensional
    analysis to find how many feet are in 42 inches.

    $\boxed{42}\ in. \times \dfrac{\boxed{1}\ ft}{\boxed{12}\ in.} = \dfrac{\boxed{42}}{\boxed{12}}\ ft = \boxed{3.5}\ ft$

11. Kara's sandwich is __3.5__ feet long.

Find how many quarts equal 7.5 pints, using each method.

12. Use equivalent ratios.
    $\dfrac{1\ qt}{2\ pts} = \dfrac{1\ qt \times 3.75}{2\ pts \times 3.75} = \dfrac{3.75\ qts}{7.5\ pts}$

13. Use dimensional analysis.
    $7.5\ pts \times \dfrac{1\ qt}{2\ pts} = \dfrac{7.5}{2}\ qts = 3.75\ qts$

14. **Reasoning** Lexie said that it is easier to use
    dimensional analysis to change 7.5 pints to quarts.
    Tomas said it is easier to use equivalent ratios.
    What do you think? Explain.
    Sample answer: It is easier to use dimensional analysis;
    To change 7.5 pints to quarts with equivalent ratios, you
    need to decide what to multiply 2 by to get 7.5. With
    dimensional analysis, you immediately see that you
    need to divide 7.5 by 2.

170 (student p. 2)   MDIS 2.0

Teacher Column

Objective Students will use ratio reasoning to convert measurements.

Vocabulary Dimensional analysis, conversion factor

1 Conceptual Development
Use with Exercises 1–11.

In this lesson, you will use ratio reasoning to convert measurements from one unit to another.

Revisit the terms *dimensional analysis* and *conversion factor* as needed. Have students work in pairs to complete Exercises 1–11. Discuss the two methods that can be used when using ratio reasoning to convert measurements. *In Exercises 1–3, what was the conversion factor used to convert gallons to cups?* 16 c per 1 g *Why did you multiply both parts of the rate by 1.75?* That's how many gallons there were. *How could you solve the problem another way, using dimensional analysis?* Multiply the number of gallons by the rate: $1.75\ g \times \dfrac{16\ c}{1\ g}$

Divide out the common units: $1.75 \times 16\ c = 28\ c$

2 Practice Use with Exercises 12–14.

Remind students that the conversion factor is a rate that is equal to 1 because the terms are equivalent measures.

Error Intervention If students have difficulty setting up the conversion with the dimensional analysis method, then tell them to multiply the given measurement by the conversion factor, which is equal to one.

If You Have More Time Discuss which exercises involve changing a larger unit to a smaller unit and which involve changing a smaller unit to a larger unit. Point out the difficulty of using equivalent ratios when changing a smaller unit to a larger one as in Exercises 4–7.

3 Assessment

In this lesson, students learned how to use ratio reasoning to convert measurements. Use the **Quick Check** problem to assess students' understanding.

Quick Check **Formative** Assessment

How many 6-inch servings are in a sandwich that is 2.5 feet long? Tell how you solve. 5 servings; Check students' work.

LINE PLOTS

Name _____

Line Plots

Materials: inch ruler for each student

Twelve fifth grade students measured their hand spans to the nearest one fourth inch. The table shows the measures they got.

Widths of Hand Spans in Inches			
$6\frac{1}{2}$	$6\frac{3}{4}$	$5\frac{3}{4}$	$5\frac{1}{4}$
$7\frac{1}{2}$	$6\frac{1}{2}$	$6\frac{3}{4}$	$6\frac{1}{4}$
$6\frac{1}{4}$	$7\frac{1}{4}$	6	$6\frac{3}{4}$

1. What is a reasonable scale for a line plot of the data in the table? How do you know? Sample answer: From 5 to 8 by fourths; All of the data values fall between 5 and 8. Using fourths will give a tick mark for each value.

2. Make a line plot of the data in the table. Sample line plot is shown.

Widths of Hand Spans in Inches

$5 \quad 5\frac{1}{4} \quad 5\frac{1}{2} \quad 5\frac{3}{4} \quad 6 \quad 6\frac{1}{4} \quad 6\frac{1}{2} \quad 6\frac{3}{4} \quad 7 \quad 7\frac{1}{4} \quad 7\frac{1}{2} \quad 7\frac{3}{4} \quad 8$

Use the line plot you made to answer the questions.

3. Which width occurred the most often? How can you use the line plot to tell? $6\frac{3}{4}$ inches occurred most often; Sample answer: There are more dots above $6\frac{3}{4}$ in the line plot than above any other number.

4. How many students had a hand span of $6\frac{1}{4}$ inches? _____2_____

5. What is the difference between the greatest hand span and the least hand span? Show how you solve. $2\frac{1}{4}$ inches; $7\frac{1}{2} - 5\frac{1}{4} = 7\frac{2}{4} - 5\frac{1}{4} = 2\frac{1}{4}$

171 (student p. 1)   MDIS 2.0

Name _____

Line Plots (continued)

The twelve students also measured the length of their index fingers to the nearest $\frac{1}{8}$ of an inch. The table shows the measures they got.

Lengths of Index Fingers in Inches			
$2\frac{1}{2}$	$2\frac{3}{8}$	$2\frac{3}{4}$	$1\frac{7}{8}$
$1\frac{5}{8}$	$2\frac{5}{8}$	$2\frac{3}{8}$	$2\frac{1}{4}$
$2\frac{1}{4}$	2	$2\frac{3}{4}$	$2\frac{3}{8}$

6. What is a reasonable scale for a line plot of the data in the table? How do you know? Sample answer: From $1\frac{1}{2}$ to 3 by eighths; All of the data values fall between $1\frac{1}{2}$ and 3. Using eighths will give a tick mark for each value.

7. Make a line plot of the data in the table. Sample line plot is shown.

Lengths of Index Fingers in Inches

$1\frac{1}{2} \quad 1\frac{5}{8} \quad 1\frac{3}{4} \quad 1\frac{7}{8} \quad 2 \quad 2\frac{1}{8} \quad 2\frac{1}{4} \quad 2\frac{3}{8} \quad 2\frac{1}{2} \quad 2\frac{5}{8} \quad 2\frac{3}{4} \quad 2\frac{7}{8} \quad 3$

Use the line plot you made to answer the questions.

8. Which length occurred the most often? $2\frac{3}{8}$ inches

9. What is the difference between the greatest length and the least length? $1\frac{1}{8}$ inches

10. **Reasoning** Tessa said that the combined length of all 5 of her fingers on one hand should be less than 5 times the length of her index finger. Tessa had the second shortest index finger. The combined length of all 5 of her fingers is less than what length? Show how you solved.
$9\frac{3}{8}$ inches; $5 \times 1\frac{7}{8} = (5 \times 1) + \left(5 \times \frac{7}{8}\right)$
$= 5 + \frac{35}{8} = 5 + 4\frac{3}{8} = 9\frac{3}{8}$

171 (student p. 2)   MDIS 2.0

Objective Students will make a line plot of measurement data and use it to solve problems.
Materials Inch ruler
Vocabulary Line plot, data, outlier, frequency table

1 Conceptual Development
Use with Exercises 1–5.

In this lesson, you will learn how to make line plots of measurement data and solve problems using them.

Have students work in pairs to complete Exercises 1–5. *What is the first thing you should do to organize this data?* Order the values from least to greatest or greatest to least *How could you use a frequency table to help?* List the hand widths in order in the table and make a tally to show how many of each. *What do the tally marks tell you?* How many dots to put above each value on the number line. Point out that the scale of the line plot could be based on half inches or whole inches, but that the plot is easier to read if there is a tick mark for each individual data value. Show the line plot on the board as you discuss students' answers.

2 Practice Use with Exercises 6–10.

Remind students that there is more than one scale that can be used, but the scale should include all the data values.

Error Intervention
If students have difficulty spacing the tick marks evenly, then encourage them to use the ruler to measure and mark distances, making them one-fourth inch apart.

If You Have More Time
Discuss whether or not each set of data has an outlier.

3 Assessment

In this lesson, students learned how to make a line plot with measurements to fractions of an inch. They also solved problems using the data in the line plot. Use the **Quick Check** problem to assess students' understanding.

Quick Check   **Formative Assessment**

What scale would you use for a line plot if the students measured their finger lengths to the nearest fourth inch and got the following data?
$2\frac{1}{2}, 1\frac{3}{4}, 2\frac{1}{4}, 2\frac{1}{4}, 2\frac{3}{4}, 2, 2\frac{3}{4}, 2\frac{1}{2}, 2\frac{3}{4}, 2, 2\frac{1}{4}, 2\frac{1}{2}$
Sample answer: from 1 to 3 by fourths

Name ______________________

Intervention Lesson 172

Combining Volumes

Nabeel's room has a window seat. A model of his room is shown.

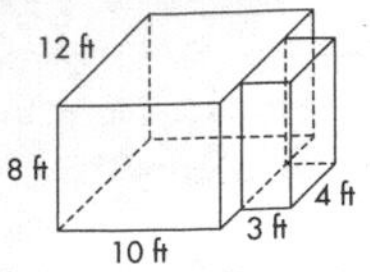

12 ft
8 ft
10 ft
3 ft
4 ft

1. What is the volume of the main part of Nabeel's room?

   $V = l \times w \times h$

   $V =$ 12 $\times$ 10 $\times$ 8 $=$ 960 cubic feet

2. What is the volume of the window seat?

   $V = l \times w \times h$

   $V =$ 4 $\times$ 3 $\times$ 8 $=$ 96 cubic feet

3. What is the total volume of Nabeel's room?

   960 $+$ 96 $=$ 1,056 cubic feet

4. Tariq used cardboard boxes to build a playhouse for his little sister. The dimensions of the boxes are shown. What is the volume of the playhouse?

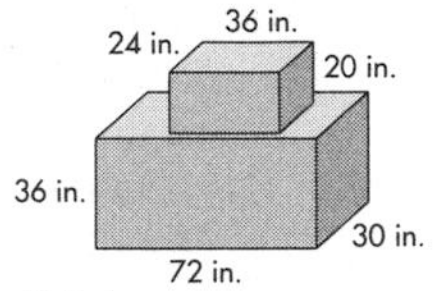

24 in.
36 in.
20 in.
36 in.
30 in.
72 in.

Big Box: $V = l \times w \times h$

$V =$ 72 $\times$ 30 $\times$ 36 $=$ 77,760 cubic inches

Little Box: $V = l \times w \times h$

$V =$ 36 $\times$ 24 $\times$ 20 $=$ 17,280 cubic inches

Total volume: 77,760 $+$ 17,280 $=$ 95,040 cubic inches

Name ______________________

Intervention Lesson 172

Combining Volumes (continued)

Find the volume of each solid figure. Show your work. Sample work is shown.

5. $V =$ 525 cm^3

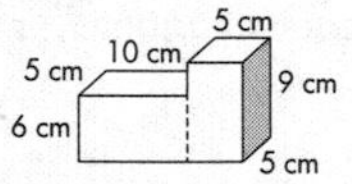

5 cm
10 cm
5 cm
9 cm
6 cm
5 cm

$V = 10 \times 5 \times 6 = 300\ cm^3$

$V = 5 \times 5 \times 9 = 225\ cm^3$

$300 + 225 = 525\ cm^3$

6. $V =$ 1,652 ft^3

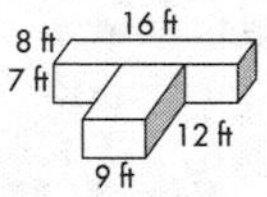

16 ft
8 ft
7 ft
12 ft
9 ft

$V = 16 \times 8 \times 7 = 896\ ft^3$

$V = 12 \times 9 \times 7 = 756\ ft^3$

$896 + 756 = 1,652\ ft^3$

7. $V =$ 395 m^3

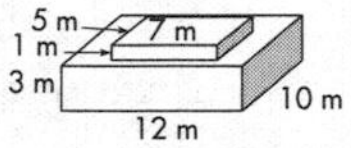

5 m
7 m
1 m
3 m
10 m
12 m

$V = 12 \times 10 \times 3 = 360\ m^3$

$V = 7 \times 5 \times 1 = 35\ m^3$

$360 + 35 = 395\ m^3$

8. What is the volume of the jewelry box shown? Show your work.

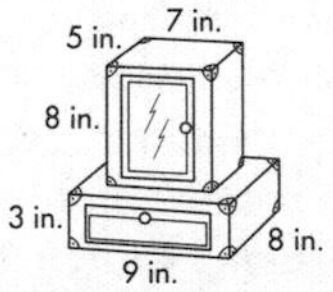

5 in.
7 in.
8 in.
3 in.
8 in.
9 in.

   $V = 9 \times 8 \times 3 = 216\ in.^3$

   $V = 7 \times 5 \times 8 = 280\ in.^3$

   $216 + 280 = 469\ in.^3$

9. **Reasoning** Which solid has a greater volume? Explain how you can tell without calculating.

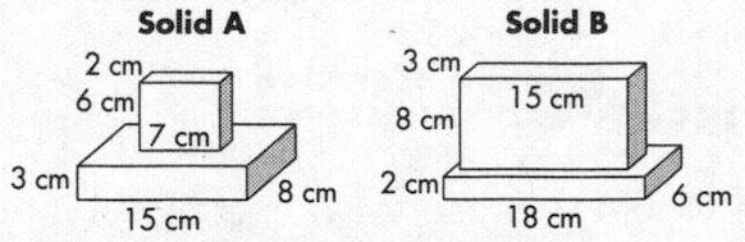

Solid A
2 cm
6 cm
7 cm
3 cm
8 cm
15 cm
Solid B
3 cm
15 cm
8 cm
2 cm
6 cm
18 cm

   Solid B has a greater volume; Sample answer: Both solids have a lower rectangular prism with equal volumes. The top prism has a volume of $7 \times 6 \times 2$ in Solid A and $15 \times 8 \times 3$ in solid B. Since $15 > 7$, Solid B has a greater volume.

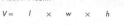

Objective Students will find the volume of solid figures that are made up of rectangular prisms.

Materials Colored pencils or markers (optional)

Vocabulary Volume, rectangular prism, formula, cubic unit, unit cube

1 Conceptual Development

Use with Exercises 1–4.

In this lesson, you will find the volume of solid figures made of rectangular prisms.

Have students work in pairs to complete Exercises 1–3. Discuss the steps taken to find the volume. *Why did it take three steps to find the volume of Nabeel's room?* Because his room combines two different rectangular prisms. We had to find the separate volume of each prism, then add them together. Then have students use those steps to complete Exercise 4. *Why is the volume of the playhouse measured in cubic inches?* Volume is the number of cubic units needed to fill a solid figure.

2 Practice **Use with Exercises 5–9.**

Remind students that the formula $V = l \times w \times h$ is only for rectangular prisms.

Error Intervention If students have difficulty interpreting the figures, then have them color the rectangular prisms two different colors and highlight the dimensions of each with matching colors.

If You Have More Time Have students find the volume of the solid in Exercise 5 a different way. If necessary, discuss how to find missing measures.

3 Assessment

In this lesson, students learned how to find the volume of a rectangular solid by using the additive nature of volume. Use the **Quick Check** problem to assess students' understanding.

Quick Check Formative Assessment

To create a statue, Nora set one block of clay on top of another. One block was 5 inches by 5 inches by 6 inches and the other was 4 inches by 4 inches by 6 inches. What was the total volume of the clay?
246 $in.^3$

Name _____

Intervention
Lesson **173**

Polygons on the Coordinate Plane

Henry's mother is planning a new city park.
The park will be in the shape of a polygon with
vertices at $(-4, 3)$, $(3, 3)$, $(3, -4)$, and $(-4, -2)$.

1. Draw a diagram of the park. Graph the points
   on the coordinate grid and then connect them
   to form a polygon. Label the points with their
   coordinates.

2. The distance between $(-4, 3)$ and $(3, 3)$ =
   $|-4| + |3| = \underline{\quad4\quad} + \underline{\quad3\quad} = \underline{\quad7\quad}$

3. The distance between $(-4, 3)$ and $(-4, -2)$ =
   $|3| + |-2| = \underline{\quad3\quad} + \underline{\quad2\quad} = \underline{\quad5\quad}$

4. The distance between $(3, 3)$ and $(3, -4)$ =
   $|3| + |-4| = \underline{\quad3\quad} + \underline{\quad4\quad} = \underline{\quad7\quad}$

5. Draw a dashed line to divide the polygon into a rectangle
   and a triangle. Find the area of the rectangle. Use the
   distances you found for the lengths of the sides.

   $A = l \cdot w$

   $= \underline{\quad7\quad} \cdot \underline{\quad5\quad} = \underline{\quad35\quad}$ m^2

6. How can you find the height of the triangle?
   Sample answer: Subtract $7 - 5 = 2$ m.

7. Find the area of the triangle.

   $A = \frac{1}{2} \cdot b \cdot h$

   $= \frac{1}{2} \cdot \underline{\quad7\quad} \cdot \underline{\quad2\quad} = \underline{\quad7\quad}$ m^2

8. What is the area of the park?

   $\underline{\quad35\quad} + \underline{\quad7\quad} = \underline{\quad42\quad}$ m^2

173 (student p. 1)   MDIS 2.0

Name _____

Intervention
Lesson **173**

Polygons on the Coordinate Plane (continued)

Find the area of each polygon. Explain how you found
the area.

9. A = ___36 ft^2___

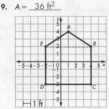

Area of rectangle = $6 \cdot 5 = 30$

Area of triangle = $\frac{1}{2} \cdot 6 \cdot 2 = 6$

Total area = $30 + 6 = 36$

10. A = ___40 cm^3___

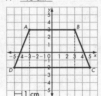

Area of rectangle = $6 \cdot 5 = 30$

Area of each triangle
$= \frac{1}{2} \cdot 2 \cdot 5 = 5$

Total area = $30 + 5 + 5 = 40$

11. **Reasoning** Kenna is designing a headscarf
    for her doll on a coordinate grid. The scarf
    will be in the shape of a polygon with
    vertices at $(-2, 4)$, $(2, 4)$, $(4, 1)$, and $(-4, 1)$.

    • Graph these points on the grid.
    • Draw dashed lines to divide the polygon
      into rectangles and triangles.
    • Show how to find the area of each part and
      the total area.

    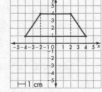

    Area of rectangle = $4 \cdot 3 = 12$

    Area of each triangle $= \frac{1}{2} \cdot 3 \cdot 2 = 3$

    Total area = $12 + 3 + 3 = 18$ cm^2

173 (student p. 2)   MDIS 2.0

Objective Students will find the area of a polygon
on a coordinate plane.

Vocabulary Coordinate plane, quadrants,
absolute value, rational numbers

1 Conceptual Development
Use with Exercises 1–8.

*In this lesson, you will find the area of polygons on a
coordinate plane.*

Have students work in pairs to complete Exercises 1–4.
*Are any of the vertices of this polygon in the same
quadrant?* No *What value do you use to calculate
the length of each sides?* The absolute value of the
distance between coordinates. *How could you find the
area of this polygon?* Decompose the polygon into a
rectangle and a triangle and use area formulas. Have
students complete Exercises 5–8.

2 Practice Use with Exercises 9–11.

Remind students that they can add or subtract the
absolute value of coordinates to find the lengths of the
sides, or they can count spaces.

Error Intervention If students have difficulty
finding the height of a triangle within the polygons,
then have them draw it with a dashed line.

If You Have More Time Have students
explain how to use the coordinates to find the lengths
needed for the formulas in Exercise 9.

3 Assessment

In this lesson, students learned how to find the area
of a polygon on a coordinate grid by decomposing
it. Use the **Quick Check** problem to assess students'
understanding.

Quick Check **Formative**
Assessment

What would be the area of the doll's scarf if Kenna
placed the vertices at $(-2, 5)$, $(2, 5)$, $(4, 1)$, and
$(-4, 1)$? 24 cm^2

Worksheet (Student pages)

Name _____

Intervention Lesson **174**

Statistical Questions

The sixth grade class is taking a survey about colors. They need to ask a statistical question, one where they can expect to get different answers.

Decide whether or not the following is a statistical question.

What are the primary colors?

1. Would people give the same or different answers to this question? Explain.
   Most people would say that the primary colors are red, blue, and yellow.

2. Is this a statistical question? __No__

Decide whether or not the following is a statistical question.

What is your favorite color?

3. Would people give the same or different answers to this question? Explain.
   Sample answer: Different people have different favorite colors, so people would give different answers.

4. Is this a statistical question? __Yes__

You can expect variability in the answers to a statistical question. The answers vary from one person to another.

Decide whether or not each of the following is a statistical question. Explain your answer for each.

5. What color are the walls in your math classroom?
   This is a not a statistical question; Sample answer: Most people in the class would say the same color.

6. How many colors do you have in your wardrobe, that is, in the clothes you wear?
   This is a statistical question; Sample answer: Some people wear more colors than others.

174 (student p. 1)   MDIS 2.0

Name _____

Intervention Lesson **174**

Statistical Questions (continued)

Choose a book to use. Answer the following questions.

7. How many words are in a paragraph? Give the count for 6 paragraphs.
   Answers will vary, but students should give 6 numbers.

8. How many words are in the title?
   Answers will vary, but students should give 1 number.

Explain your answer for each.

9. Is the question in Exercise 7 statistical?
   Yes; Sample answer: You expect different answers depending on which paragraphs you look at.

10. Is the question in Exercise 8 statistical?
    No; Sample answer: Although there are different paragraphs in a book, there is only one title. Thus, the number of words in the title is always the same for a given book.

11. Would it make more sense to draw a graph of the data in Exercise 7 or the data in Exercise 8? Justify your answer.
    The data in Exercise 7; Sample answer: There is only one number in the data set in Exercise 8 so there is no point in drawing a graph.

12. **Reasoning** Write a statistical question you could ask people in your class.
    Answers will vary. Check that students' questions are statistical.

13. Ask 10 people your statistical question and list the answers here. Make a bar graph of the results.
    Answers will vary. Check for reasonableness and accuracy in creating the bar graph.

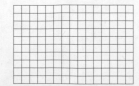

174 (student p. 2)   MDIS 2.0

Objective Students will identify and write statistical questions.
Vocabulary Statistical question

➊ Conceptual Development
Use with Exercises 1–6.

In this lesson, you will decide whether or not a question is statistical and write statistical questions.

Discuss Exercises 1–4 as a group. Help students understand the concept of variability. *Is there one correct answer to a statistical question?* No; if it has one correct answer, it is not a statistical question. *Is it possible to get the same answer from everyone when you ask a statistical question like "What is your favorite color?"* It is possible, but not likely; we ask the question because we expect a variety of responses. Have students work in pairs to complete Exercises 5 and 6. Discuss as needed. You may want to point out that the question in Exercise 5 could become a statistical question if it were asked of students across the entire country.

➋ Practice Use with Exercises 7–13.

Remind students that in order for a question to be statistical, answers to the question must vary depending on who you ask.

Error Intervention If students have difficulty interpreting Exercises 7 and 8, then emphasize that they should choose just one specific book. Ask if there is more than one paragraph and more than one title.

If You Have More Time Have students write more statistical questions and work as a group to check that each one anticipates variability in the responses.

➌ Assessment

In this lesson, students learned how to identify and write statistical questions. Use the **Quick Check** problem to assess students' understanding.

Quick Check   Formative Assessment

"How many times do you shampoo your hair each week?" Is this a statistical question? Explain why or why not. It is a statistical question; Sample answer: Different people will likely give different answers.

Box Plots

Nine students measured the length of one hair on their heads to the nearest inch. They got the following results.

4, 8, 0, 1, 4, 0, 3, 2, 5

1. Write the numbers in the boxes below, in order from least to greatest.

0	0	1	2	3	4	4	5	8

↑minimum   ↑median   ↑maximum

2. The least number is the minimum. What is the minimum hair length?   __0__ in.

3. The greatest number is the maximum. What is the maximum hair length?   __8__ in.

4. The median is the middle number when the data are listed in order from least to greatest. What is the median hair length?   __3__ in.

5. Write the numbers that are below the median in the boxes. Keep them in order from least to greatest.

0	0	1	2

Remember, to find the median of an even number of data values, you find the average of the two middle numbers.

6. What is the median of the numbers in Exercise 5, in decimal form?

$$\frac{\boxed{0}+\boxed{1}}{2} = \frac{\boxed{1}}{2} = \boxed{0.5}$$

This is the first quartile. It is the median of the numbers below the median of the data set.

7. The third quartile is the median of the numbers above the median of the data set. What is the third quartile?

$$\frac{\boxed{4}+\boxed{5}}{2} = \frac{\boxed{9}}{2} = \boxed{4.5}$$

   175 (student p. 1)   MDIS 2.0

Box Plots (continued)

8. Draw a box plot of the hair length data. Follow these steps.

 • Use a number line with an appropriate scale, like the one below.
 • Draw a box between the first and third quartiles.
 • Draw a vertical line in the box at the median.
 • Put points at the minimum and maximum values and draw segments from these points to the box.

0 1 2 3 4 5 6 7 8 9

The box plot divides the data into fourths. So, $\frac{1}{4}$ or 25% of the data is between 0 and 0.5. Another 25% is between 0.5 and 3, another between 3 and 4.5, and another between 4.5 and 8.

Ten students counted how many times their hearts beat in 15 seconds. They got the following results.

15, 18, 14, 21, 18, 20, 16, 19, 16, 16

9. Write the numbers in the boxes below, in order from least to greatest. Use this to find the minimum, maximum, median, and the first and third quartiles.

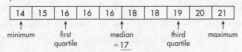

14	15	16	16	16	18	18	19	20	21

↑minimum   ↑first quartile   ↑median =17   ↑third quartile   ↑maximum

10. **Reasoning** Draw a box plot of the heartbeat data.

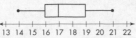

13 14 15 16 17 18 19 20 21 22

   175 (student p. 2)   MDIS 2.0

Objective Students will make and analyze box plots.

Vocabulary Box plot, quartiles

① Conceptual Development
Use with Exercises 1–8.

In this lesson, you will draw and interpret a box plot.

Have students work in pairs to complete Exercises 1–8. In a group discussion, ask students to explain how they found each of the 5 data points used to draw the box plot. Also, make sure students understand how the plot divides the data into fourths, or quartiles. *How do you find the first and third quartiles?* Find the median for each half of the data. You may want to point out in the final box plot (Exercise 8) that the clustering of three quartiles toward the left end of the number line tells us that the hair lengths were generally shorter rather than longer.

② Practice Use with Exercises 9–10.

Remind students that the first quartile is the median of the numbers below the median of the data set. For the heartbeat data, this is the median of 14, 15, 16, 16, 16.

Error Intervention
If students have difficulty finding the median, then remind them to add the two middle values and divide by 2.

If You Have More Time
Ask students to name the middle range of the data where 50% of the data values lie. This will help them interpret box plots and find interquartile range.

③ Assessment

In this lesson, students learned how to make and analyze box plots. Use the **Quick Check** problem to assess students' understanding.

Quick Check   **Formative** Assessment

Why did you need to add and divide by 2 to find the median for the heart beat data but not for the hair length data? There were an odd number of values in the hair length data, so one value was in the middle. However, the heartbeat data had an even number of values, so two numbers were in the middle.

Student Page 1

Name _____

Intervention
Lesson **176**

Measures of Variability

The girls on the middle school basketball team have the following heights, in inches.

59, 61, 57, 58, 60, 59, 58, 60, 62, 56

1. What is the mean height? ___59 in.___

2. Complete the table to find the difference between each data value and the mean.

Score	Absolute Deviation
56	$\lvert 59 - 56 \rvert = 3$
57	$\lvert 59 - 57 \rvert = 2$
58	$\lvert 59 - 58 \rvert = 1$
58	$\lvert 59 - 58 \rvert = 1$
59	$\lvert 59 - 59 \rvert = 0$
59	$\lvert 59 - 59 \rvert = 0$
60	$\lvert 60 - 59 \rvert = 1$
60	$\lvert 60 - 59 \rvert = 1$
61	$\lvert 61 - 59 \rvert = 2$
62	$\lvert 62 - 59 \rvert = 3$

3. What is the mean of these differences? Show your work.

$1.4; \dfrac{3 + 2 + 1 + 1 + 0 + 0 + 1 + 1 + 2 + 3}{10} =$
$\dfrac{14}{10} = 1.4$

This is the mean absolute deviation (MAD). It is a measure of variability. Since the MAD is a small number, it indicates that the heights of the girls on the team do not vary much. They are all close to the same height.

4. Write the heights in the boxes below, in order from least to greatest. Use this to find the minimum, maximum, median, and the first and third quartiles.

56	57	58	58	59	59	60	60	61	62

↑ minimum   ↑ first quartile   ↑ median = 59   ↑ third quartile   ↑ maximum

5. Draw a box plot of the height data.

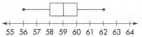

55 56 57 58 59 60 61 62 63 64

176 (student p. 1)   MDIS 2.0

Student Page 2

Name _____

Intervention
Lesson **176**

Measures of Variability (continued)

6. What is the difference of the first and third quartiles? ___60 − 58 = 2___

This is the interquartile range (IQR). It is also a measure of variability. Like the MAD, the IQR indicates that the heights do not vary much.

7. What percent of the heights are within an interval equal to the IQR? ___50%___

In the first 6 games, the basketball team scored the following numbers of points.

25, 30, 45, 26, 32, 28

Score	Absolute Deviation
25	$\lvert 31 - 25 \rvert = 6$
26	$\lvert 31 - 26 \rvert = 5$
28	$\lvert 31 - 28 \rvert = 3$
30	$\lvert 31 - 30 \rvert = 1$
32	$\lvert 32 - 31 \rvert = 1$
45	$\lvert 45 - 31 \rvert = 14$

8. What is the mean absolute deviation? Explain how you found it. ___5___ points

$\dfrac{25 + 30 + 45 + 26 + 32 + 28}{6} = \dfrac{186}{6} = 31$

$\dfrac{6 + 5 + 3 + 1 + 1 + 14}{6} = \dfrac{30}{6} = 5$

9. What is the interquartile range? Explain how you found it. ___6___ points

25	26	28	30	32	45

↑ minimum   ↑ first quartile   ↑ median   ↑ third quartile   ↑ maximum

$32 - 26 = 6$

10. **Reasoning** Does the outlier 45 have more effect on the MAD or the IQR? Justify your answer.
The outlier has more effect on the MAD; Sample answer: The IQR would be the same whether the maximum value was 33 or 45. However, the outlier adds a lot to the total divided by 6 to get the MAD.

176 (student p. 2)   MDIS 2.0

Teacher Column

Objective Students will find mean absolute deviation and interquartile range.
Vocabulary Mean absolute deviation (MAD), interquartile range (IQR)

① Conceptual Development
Use with Exercises 1–7.

In this lesson, you will find the mean absolute deviation and the interquartile range for a set of data.

Have students work in pairs to complete Exercises 1–7. Discuss how the MAD and IQR indicate variability of data. *What does the mean absolute deviation tell you about the variability in a data set?* MAD describes how far a typical value is from the mean. A low number shows not much variability; a high number shows the data are more spread out. *How does the interquartile range indicate the amount of variability in a data set?* The IQR shows half of the data. Again, a small number shows the data are clustered close to the mean; a large number shows the data are more spread out, or more variable. Make sure students understand that in the girls' basketball team data, 50% of the heights fall in an interval of 2 inches.

② Practice Use with Exercises 8–10.

Remind students that to find the difference between a score and the mean, they can subtract the number that is less from the greater number.

Error Intervention If students don't remember how to find the mean, then remind them to add the scores and then divide by the number of scores.

If You Have More Time Tell students that the heights of the boys on the middle school basketball team have a MAD of 2.5. Ask students which varies more, the heights of the boys or the heights of the girls. Have them explain how they know.

③ Assessment

In this lesson, students learned how to calculate two measures of variability. Use the **Quick Check** problem to assess students' understanding.

Quick Check Formative Assessment

Refer the points the basketball team scored in 6 games: 25, 30, 45, 26, 32, 28. Suppose that instead of 45 points, the team had scored 27 points in that game. What would the MAD be then? 2 points

APPROPRIATE USE OF STATISTICAL MEASURES

Name _____

Intervention Lesson **177**

Appropriate Use of Statistical Measures

Two teams of sixth grade students had a contest to see which team could type the most words on a computer keyboard in 15 seconds. Each team had 10 members. The results are shown in the table.

Words Typed										
Rockets	7	8	6	9	10	20	6	7	7	5
Pacers	11	12	9	8	7	8	12	8	7	8

1. What is the mean number of words the Rockets typed? Show your work.
   8.5 words; 85 ÷ 10 = 8.5

2. What is the median number of words the Rockets typed? ___7 words___

3. Does the mean or the median give a better indication of the typical number of words the Rockets typed? Justify your answer.
   The median; The mean is a little high because of the outlier, 20.

4. What is the mean number of words the Pacers typed? Show your work.
   9 words; 90 ÷ 10 = 9

5. What is the median number of words the Pacers typed? ___8 words___

6. Does the mean or the median give a better indication of the typical number of words the Pacers typed? Justify your answer.
   The mean; The median is a little low. The mean does a better job of including all the amounts, and in this data set, it is not distorted by an outlier.

When the median is the best measure of center, use the interquartile range (IQR) to measure the variability. When the mean is the best measure of center, use the mean absolute deviation (MAD) to measure variability.

7. What is the IQR for the number of words the Rockets typed? ___3___

177 (student p. 1) MDIS 2.0

Name _____

Intervention Lesson **177**

Appropriate Use of Statistical Measures (continued)

8. What is the MAD for the number of words the Pacers typed? Use the table to help you find it.

   MAD = ___1.6 words___

Words	Absolute Deviation
7	|9 − 7| = 2
7	|9 − 7| = 2
8	|9 − 8| = 1
8	|9 − 8| = 1
8	|9 − 8| = 1
8	|9 − 8| = 1
9	|9 − 9| = 0
11	|11 − 9| = 2
12	|12 − 9| = 3
12	|12 − 9| = 3

9. The MAD for the Rockets is 2.7. Which team had more variability in the number of words the members typed?
   ___Rockets___

The table shows the speeds of 5 practice serves by two tennis players.

Serve Speed (in mph)					
Joe	46	50	49	52	48
Andy	45	60	50	47	43

10. What is the mean speed of Joe's serves?
    ___49 mph___

11. What is the median speed of Joe's serves?
    ___49 mph___

12. What is the mean speed of Andy's serves?
    ___49 mph___

13. What is the median speed of Andy's serves?
    ___47 mph___

14. Who has a faster serve on average, Joe or Andy? Use a measure of center to justify your answer.
    Joe; The means are the same, but the median speed of Joe's serves is higher than the median speed of Andy's serves.

15. Does the mean or the median give a better indication of the typical speed of Andy's serves?
    Median; The mean is a little high because of the outlier of 60.

16. **Reasoning** Whose serve is more consistent? Use IQR to justify your answer.
    Joe's serve; The IQR for Joe's serves is 51 − 47 = 4. The IQR for Andy's serves is 55 − 44 = 11. Since 4 < 11 there is less variability in Joe's serve than in Andy's serve. Joe's serve is more consistent.

177 (student p. 2) MDIS 2.0

Objective Students will select and use appropriate statistical measures.

Vocabulary Mean absolute deviation (MAD), interquartile range (IQR)

1 Conceptual Development
Use with Exercises 1–9.

In this lesson, you will choose appropriate measures of center and variability.

Have students work in pairs to complete Exercises 1–6. Review the terms *mean* and *median* as necessary. Discuss Exercises 3 and 6, being sure students understand which measure of center more accurately describe each data set. *If the teams used the mean to determine the winner, who would win?* Pacers *Who would win if they used the median?* Pacers *Which team had the fastest typist?* Rockets *Why didn't that team win?* Because the fastest speed is an outlier; most of the Rockets typed slower overall than the other team. Have students work in pairs to complete Exercises 7–9.

2 Practice Use with Exercises 10–16.

Remind students that a small IQR or MAD indicates little variability.

Error Intervention
If students have difficulty finding the IQRs, then remind them the first quartile is the median of the numbers below the median of the whole data set. For Joe's serve speed, the IQR is the median of 46, 48.

If You Have More Time
Have students use the MAD to decide whether Joe's or Andy's serve is more consistent.

3 Assessment

In this lesson, students learned how to select and use appropriate statistical measures. Use the **Quick Check** problem to assess students' understanding.

Quick Check
Formative Assessment

Ella had serve speeds of 58, 57, 45, 56, 60 mph. Would the mean or median be a better measure of center to use for Ella's serve speeds? Explain. The median, 57, is a better measure. The mean, 55.2, is affected by the outlier of 46 and makes Ella's typical speed seem lower than it really is.

177 MDIS 2.0

Name _____

Summarize Data Distributions

Intervention
Lesson **178**

A data distribution is how the values are arranged in a data set.
To describe a data distribution you:

- give a measure of center,
- give a measure of variability,
- describe the overall shape of the data, and
- sometimes show the data in a graph.

Eight students each shot 20 basketball free throws. The list
shows how many free throw shots they made.

10, 9, 8, 10, 15, 5, 9, 14

1. What is the mean number of free throws the players made?
   Show your work.
   10 baskets; 80 ÷ 8 = 10

2. Write the data in the boxes below, in order from least to greatest. Use this
   to find the minimum, maximum, median, and the first and third quartiles.

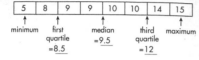

Since the mean and the median are close, either one is appropriate.

3. Draw a box plot of the free throw data.

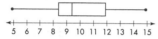

4. What is the IQR for the number of free throws
   the students made?   3.5 baskets

178 (student p. 1)   MDIS 2.0

Name _____

Summarize Data Distributions (continued)

Intervention
Lesson **178**

5. Describe the overall shape of the data by answering the following
   questions.

   - Are the data values symmetric or more spread out to either
     the right or the left?
   - Are there any gaps in the data?
   - Where are most of the data values grouped?

   Sample answer: The data values are more spread out to the
   right. There are gaps between 5 and 8 and between 10 and 14.
   Most of the data values are grouped between 8 and 10.

Eight students did a standing high jump. The data show
how far they jumped, in inches.

16, 11, 19, 10, 16, 21, 12, 15

Describe the data distribution by answering the following.

6. What is the mean number of inches the students jumped?
   Show your work.
   15 inches; 120 ÷ 8 = 15

7. What is the MAD for the number of
   inches the students jumped? Use the
   table to help you find it.

   MAD = __3 inches__

Inches Jumped	Absolute Deviation
10	|15 − 10| = 5
11	|15 − 11| = 4
12	|15 − 12| = 3
15	|15 − 15| = 0
16	|16 − 15| = 1
16	|16 − 15| = 1
19	|19 − 15| = 4
21	|21 − 15| = 6

8. Make a dot plot of the data to help you see
   the overall shape of the distribution.

9. **Reasoning** Describe the overall shape of the
   data distribution.
   Sample answer: The data are very spread out. There are gaps
   between 12 and 15 and between 16 and 19. There is a group
   of data values at 10 to 12 and another group at 15 and 16.

178 (student p. 2)   MDIS 2.0

Objective Students will describe the distribution of
a numerical data set.
Vocabulary Data distribution, mean absolute
deviation (MAD), interquartile range (IQR)

① Conceptual Development
Use with Exercises 1–5.

In this lesson, you will describe data distributions.

Have students work in pairs to complete Exercises 1–5.
*What is a statistical question that this data might
answer?* Sample answer: Given 20 free throw shots,
what is the typical number of shots a student will
make? *How does finding the mean and median help
you describe the data distribution?* The mean and
median give a measure of center. *What did you use
for a measure of variability?* Interquartile range *What
did the IQR tell you about the data distribution?* Half
of the students made from about 8 to 12 of their shots.
Give extra attention to Exercise 5, discussing with
students how the box plot can be used to describe the
overall shape of the data.

② Practice **Use with Exercises 6–9.**

Remind students that to find the mean distance
jumped, they add the data values and divide by 8,
the number of values.

Error Intervention If students have difficulty
describing the shape of the distribution, then have
them answer the questions listed in Exercise 5.

If You Have More Time Ask students what
the mean and MAD indicate about the high jump
data. The typical height jumped was 15 inches with
a variation of 3 inches.

③ Assessment

In this lesson, students learned how to describe a data
distribution. Use the **Quick Check** problem to assess
students' understanding.

Quick Check   **Formative**
                          Assessment

Look again at the high jump data. If the student who
jumped 21 inches had only jumped 18 inches, how
would the distribution of the data change? Sample
answer: The data would be less spread out. The mean
and MAD would both be less.

Name _____

Solid Figures

Materials power solids arranged in stations around the room

Find each solid to complete the tables below.

	Solid	Number of Faces	Number of Edges	Number of Vertices	Shapes of Faces
1.	Pyramid	5	8	5	1 square 4 triangles
2.	Rectangular Prism				
3.	Cube				

Some objects that roll do not have faces, edges, or vertices.

	Solid	Number of Flat Surfaces	Shape of Flat Surfaces
4.	Cone	1	1 circle

11 (student p. 1)   MDIS 2.0

Name _____

Solid Figures (continued)

	Solid	Number of Flat Surfaces	Shape of Flat Surfaces
5.	Cylinder		
6.	Sphere		

Name the solid figure that each object looks like.

7.

8.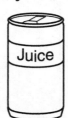

9.

_____

_____

_____

Use the solids in the table above to answer Exercises 10–12.

10. Which solid figure has 2 flat surfaces that are circles?

_____

11. Which of the 6 solid figures has 6 rectangular faces?

_____

12. Which 2 figures have no vertices?

_____

13. **Reasoning** How are the sphere and cone alike?

_____

 MDIS 2.0

Lines and Line Segments

Materials crayons, markers, or colored pencils

A point is an exact place. It is shown by a very small dot.

1. Color in the circle to show a point.   ○

A *line* is an endless number of points going on forever in two directions.
There is no beginning and no end.

2. Color over the points to make a solid line.
   Color in the two arrows to show the line
   goes on forever in both directions.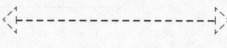

A *line segment* is a part of a line. It has a beginning and an end.

3. Color over the points to make a solid line segment.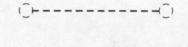
   Color in the points that are shown larger, to show
   the line segment's beginning and end. These points
   are called *endpoints*.

Box A	Box B
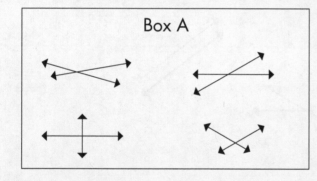	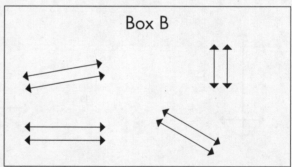

4. **Reasoning** How are the pairs of lines in Box A different
   from those in Box B?

Intersecting lines cross in a point. Parallel lines never cross.

5. What type of lines are shown in Box A?   _____

6. What type of lines are shown in Box B?   _____

12 (student p. 1)   MDIS 2.0

Lines and Line Segments (continued)

7. Circle each figure with the color named below.

   points—red   lines—blue   line segments—green

   pairs of intersecting lines—orange   pairs of parallel lines—purple

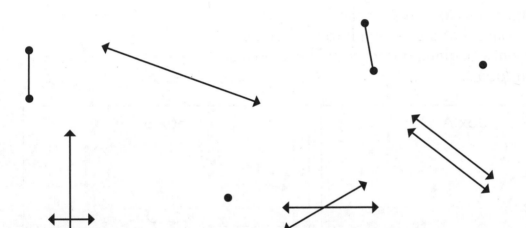

Draw an example of each.

8. parallel lines   **9.** line segment   **10.** line

12. Reasoning Draw an example of intersecting line segments.

         MDIS 2.0

Acute, Right, and Obtuse Angles

Materials 1 inch square piece of paper for each student, crayons or markers

A *ray* is part of a line. The endpoint is the beginning of the ray, and the arrow shows it goes on forever.

An *angle* is made by two rays that have the same endpoint. That endpoint is called the *vertex*.

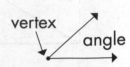

1. Color each ray of the angle at the right, a different color.

Place a side of your square on one ray, and the corner on the vertex for each angle in 2 to 4.

2. **Reasoning** *Right angles* are shown below. What do you notice about the openings of right angles?

3. **Reasoning** *Obtuse angles* are shown below. What do you notice about the openings of obtuse angles?

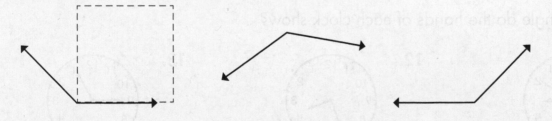

13 (student p. 1) MDIS 2.0

Name _____

Acute, Right, and Obtuse Angles (continued)

4. **Reasoning** *Acute angles* are shown below. What do you
   notice about the openings of acute angles?

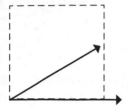   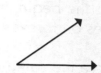

Write *ray, vertex, right angle, acute angle,* or *obtuse angle* to
name each.

5.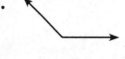

6.

7.

_____   _____   _____

8.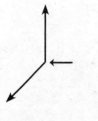

9.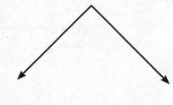

10.

_____   _____   _____

What kind of angle do the hands of each clock show?

11.

12.

13.

_____   _____   _____

13 (student p. 2)   MDIS 2.0

Name _____

Polygons

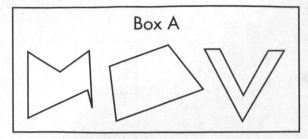
Box A

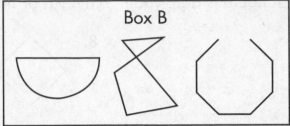
Box B

1. The figures in Box A are polygons. The figures in Box B are not.
How are the figures in Box A different from those in Box B?

To be a polygon:

- All sides must be made of straight line segments.
- Line segments must only intersect at a vertex.
- The figure must be closed.

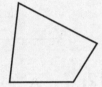

Polygons are named by the number of sides each has.
Complete the table.

	Shape	Number of Sides	Number of Vertices	Name
2.				Triangle
3.				Quadrilateral
4.				Pentagon
5.				Hexagon
6.				Octagon

 MDIS 2.0

Name _____

Polygons (continued)

Tell if each figure is a polygon. Write *yes* or *no*.

7.

_____

8.

_____

9.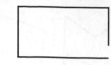

_____

Name each polygon. Then tell the number of sides and the number of vertices each polygon has.

10.

_____

11.

_____

12.

_____

13.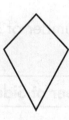

_____

14.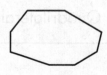

_____

15.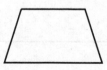

_____

16. **Reasoning** What is the least number of sides a polygon can have?

_____

17. **Reasoning** A regular polygon is a polygon with all sides the same length. Circle the figure on the right that is a regular polygon.

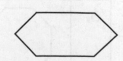

14 (student p. 2)   MDIS 2.0

Classifying Triangles Using Sides and Angles

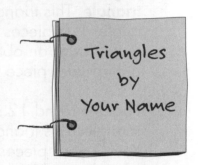

Materials 2 yards of yarn, scissors, 6 sheets of construction
paper, markers for each student and glue

Create a book about triangles by following 1 to 7.

1. Put the pieces of construction paper together and
   fold them in half to form a book. Punch two holes
   in the side and use yarn to tie the book together.
   Write "Triangles" and your name on the cover.

Each two-page spread will be about one type
of triangle. For each two page spread:

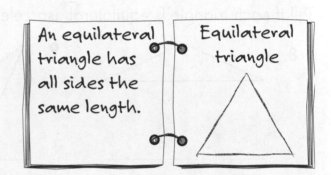

- Write the definition on the left page.
- Write the name of the triangle near
  the top of the right page.
- Create a triangle with yarn pieces and
  glue the yarn pieces under the name
  of the triangle to illustrate the triangle.

2. Pages 1 and 2 should be about an **equilateral
   triangle.** This triangle has 3 sides of equal length.
   So, your 3 yarn pieces should be cut to the same
   length.

3. Pages 3 and 4 should be about an **isosceles triangle.**
   This triangles has at least two sides the same length.
   Cut 2 pieces of yarn the same length and glue them
   on the page at an angle. Cut and glue a third piece
   to complete the triangle.

4. Pages 5 and 6 should be about a **scalene triangle.**
   This triangle has no sides the same length. So your
   3 yarn pieces can be cut to different lengths.

5. Pages 7 and 8 should be about a **right triangle.**
   This triangle has exactly one right angle. Two of
   your yarn pieces should be placed so that they
   form a right angle. Cut and glue a third piece
   to complete the triangle.

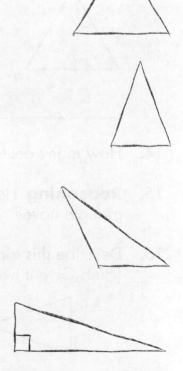

15 (student p. 1)

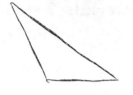
Classifying Triangles Using Sides and Angles (continued)

6. Pages 9 and 10 should be about an **obtuse triangle.** This triangle has exactly one obtuse angle. Two pieces of yarn should be placed so that it forms an obtuse angle. Cut and glue down a third yarn piece to complete the triangle.

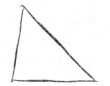

7. Pages 11 and 12 should be about an **acute triangle.** This triangle has three acute angles. Your 3 yarn pieces should be placed so that no right or obtuse angles are formed.

Tell if each triangle is equilateral, isosceles, or scalene.

8.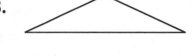

_____

9.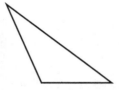

_____

10.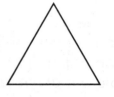

_____

Tell if each triangle is right, acute, or obtuse.

11.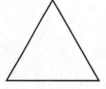

_____

12.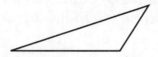

_____

13.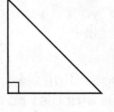

_____

14. How many acute angles does an acute triangle have? _____

15. **Reasoning** How many acute angles does a right triangle have? _____

16. Describe this triangle by its sides and by its angles. (Hint: Give it two names.)

_____ _____

15 (student p. 2)   MDIS 2.0

Name _____

Quadrilaterals

Materials Have quadrilateral power shapes available for
students who want to use them.

For 1 to 5 study each quadrilateral with your partner. Identify
the types of angles. Compare the lengths of the sides. Then
draw a line to match the quadrilateral with the best description.
Descriptions can be used only once.

1. Trapezoid

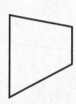

| Four right angles and all four sides the same length |

2. Parallelogram

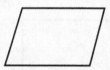

| All sides are the same length |

3. Rectangle

| Exactly one pair of parallel sides |

4. Square

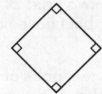

| Two pairs of parallel sides |

5. Rhombus

| Four right angles and opposite sides the same length |

6. **Reasoning** What quadrilateral has four right angles
and opposite sides the same length, and can also
be called a rectangle?   _____

7. **Reasoning** What quadrilaterals have two pairs of
parallel sides, and can also be called parallelograms?

_____

16 (student p. 1)   MDIS 2.0

Quadrilaterals (continued)

For Exercises 8–13, circle squares red, rectangles blue, parallelograms green, rhombuses orange and trapezoids purple. Some quadrilaterals may be circled more than once.

8.

9.

10.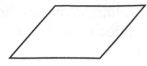

11.

12.

13.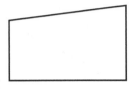

14. I have two pairs of parallel sides, and all of my sides are equal, but I have no right angles. What quadrilateral am I? _____

15. I have two pairs of parallel sides and 4 right angles, but all 4 of my sides are not equal. What quadrilateral am I? _____

16. Name all of the quadrilaterals in the picture at the right.

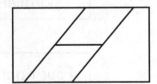

17. **Reasoning** Why is the quadrilateral on the right a parallelogram, but not a rectangle?

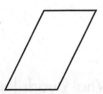

     MDIS 2.0

Name _____

Making New Shapes from Shapes

Use rhombus pattern blocks to make 1 and 2. Draw the blocks you used.

1.

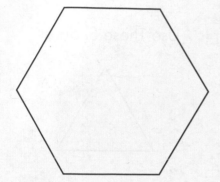

2.

Use triangle pattern blocks to make 3 and 4. Draw the blocks you used.

3.

4.

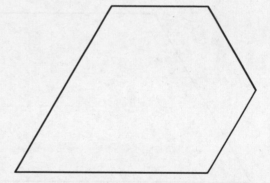

Use triangle and rhombus pattern blocks to make 5 and 6. Draw the blocks you used.

5.

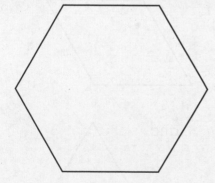

6.

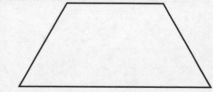

     MDIS 2.0

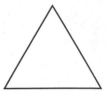

Making New Shapes from Shapes (continued)

Use pattern blocks to make each shape.
Draw the blocks you used.

Make This Shape   Use These Shapes

7.

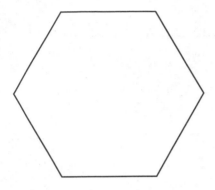

8.

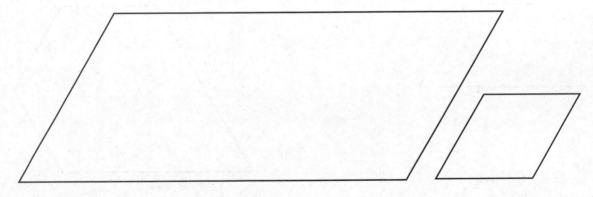

9.

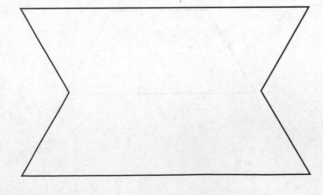

and

10.   Create your own shape.
Show the blocks you used.

     MDIS 2.0

Cutting Shapes Apart

For Exercise 1, draw 1 line to make 2 squares. For Exercise 2, draw 1 line to make 2 rectangles.

1.

2.
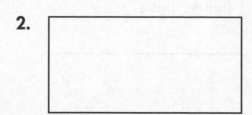

For Exercise 3, draw 1 line to make 2 triangles. For Exercise 4, draw 2 lines to make 4 triangles.

3.

4.
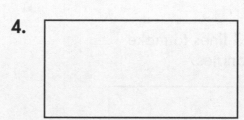

For Exercises 5 and 6, draw 2 lines to cut the parallelogram into smaller shapes two different ways. List the shapes you made.

5.
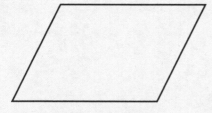

_____

6.
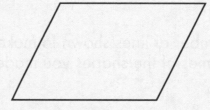

_____

For Exercises 7 and 8, draw 3 lines to cut the hexagon into smaller shapes two different ways. List the shapes you made.

7.
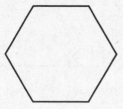

_____

8.
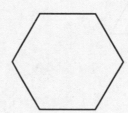

_____

   MDIS 2.0

Cutting Shapes Apart (continued)

Draw lines to make new shapes.

9. Draw 1 line to make 2 triangles.

10. Draw 2 lines to make 4 squares.

11. Draw 3 lines to make 6 rectangles.

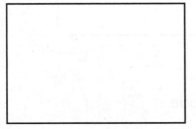

12. Draw 3 lines to make 6 triangles.

Draw the number of lines shown to make new shapes.
Write the names of the shapes you made.

13. 1 line

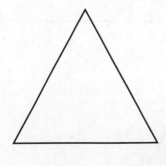

_____

14. 2 lines

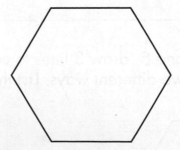

_____

     MDIS 2.0

Congruent Figures and Motions

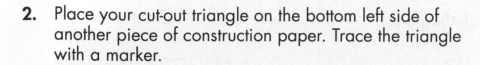

Materials construction paper, markers, and scissors

Follow 1–10.

1. Cut a scalene triangle out of construction paper.

2. Place your cut-out triangle on the bottom left side of
    another piece of construction paper. Trace the triangle
    with a marker.

Slide

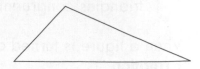

3. Slide your cut-out triangle to the upper right of the
    same paper and trace the triangle again.

4. Look at the two triangles that you just traced. Are the
    two triangles the same size and shape?

    _____

When a figure is moved up, down, left, or right, the motion is
called a **slide**, or **translation**.

Figures that are the exact same size and shape are called
congruent figures.

5. On a new sheet of paper, draw a straight dashed line as
    shown at the right. Place your cut-out triangle on the left
    side of the dashed line. Trace the triangle with a marker.

Flip

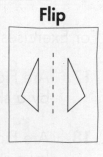

6. Pick up your triangle and flip it over the dashed line, like
    you were turning a page in a book. Trace the triangle again.

7. Look at the two triangles that you just traced. Are the
    two triangles congruent?

    _____

When a figure is picked up and flipped over, the motion is called
a **flip**, or **reflection**.

8. On a new sheet of paper, draw a point in the middle of
    the paper. Place a vertex of your cut-out triangle on
    the point. Trace the triangle with a marker.

Turn

9. Keep the vertex of your triangle on the point and move
    the triangle around the point like the hands on a clock.
    Trace the triangle again.

19 (student p. 1)   MDIS 2.0

Congruent Figures and Motions (continued)

10. Look at the two triangles you just traced. Are the two triangles congruent? _____

When a figure is turned around a point, the motion is a **turn**, or **rotation**.

Write slide, flip, or turn for each diagram.

11.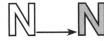

12.

13.

_____

_____

_____

14.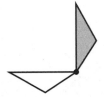

15.

16.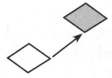

_____

_____

_____

For Exercises 17 and 18, use the figures to the right.

17. Are Figures 1 and 2 related by a slide, a flip, or a turn? _____

18. Are Figures 1 and 3 related by a slide, a flip, or a turn? _____

Figure 1

Figure 3

Figure 2

19. **Reasoning** Are the polygons at the right congruent? If so, what motion could be used to show it?

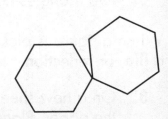

MDIS 2.0

Line Symmetry

Materials one sheet of 3″ × 3″ paper, two sheets of 2″ × 4″
paper, for each student

1. How many ways can you fold a rectangular sheet of paper
   so that the two parts match exactly?

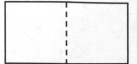 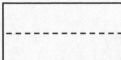

_____

A **line of symmetry** is a line on which a figure can be folded
so the two parts match exactly.

2. Fold the square sheet of paper as many ways
   as you can so the two sides match. One way
   is shown at the right. How many lines of
   symmetry does a square have?

_____

3. Cut a rectangular sheet of paper in half as
   shown at the right. Cut out one of the
   triangles formed.

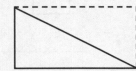

4. Fold the right triangle as many ways as you
   can so two sides match. How many lines of
   symmetry does the right triangle have?

_____

If a figure has at least one line of symmetry, it is **symmetric**.

5. Circle the figures that are symmetric.

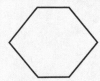   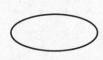

To draw a symmetric figure, flip the given half over the line of symmetry.

 MDIS 2.0

Name _____

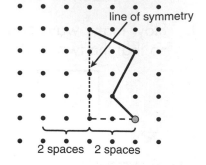

Line Symmetry (continued)

Complete the figure below to make a symmetric figure by answering 6 to 8.

6. Find a vertex that is not on the line of symmetry. Count the number of spaces from the line of symmetry to the vertex.

7. Count the same number of spaces on the other side of the line of symmetry and mark a point.

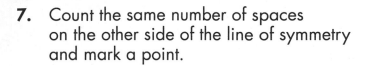

8. Use line segments to connect the new vertices. Do this until the figure is complete.

Decide whether or not each figure is symmetric. Write Yes or No

9.

10.

11.

_____   _____   _____

Complete each figure so the dotted line segment is the line of symmetry.

12.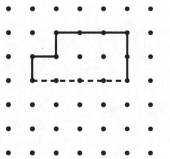

13.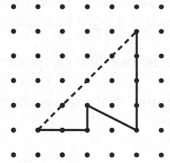

Draw all lines of symmetry for each figure.

14.

15.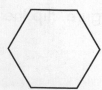

     MDIS 2.0

Solids and Nets

Materials tape, scissors, copy of nets
for all prisms, square and
rectangular pyramids from
Teaching Tool Masters

Cut out and tape each net to help
complete the tables. Each group
should make 7 solids.

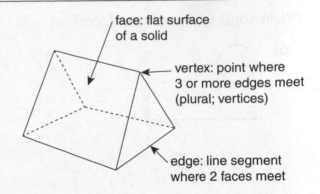

face: flat surface of a solid

vertex: point where 3 or more edges meet (plural; vertices)

edge: line segment where 2 faces meet

	Solid	Faces	Edges	Vertices	Shapes of Faces
1.	Pyramid	5	8	5	1 square 4 triangles
2.	Rectangular Pyramid				
3.	Cube				
4.	Rectangular Prism				
5.	Triangular Prism				

 MDIS 2.0

Name _____

Solids and Nets (continued)

What solid will each net form?

6.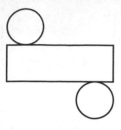

_____

7.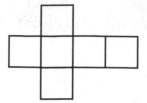

_____

8.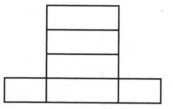

_____

9.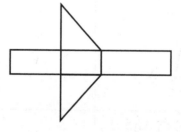

_____

10.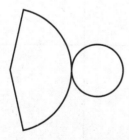

_____

11.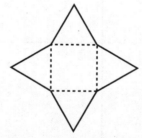

_____

12. **Reasoning** Is the figure a net for a cube? Explain.

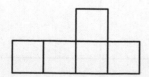

 MDIS 2.0

Views of Solid Figures

Materials 6 blocks or small cubes from place-value blocks for each pair or group, crayons or markers

Stack blocks to model the solid shown at the right. Assume that there are only 6 cubes in the solid so that none are hidden.

The top view of the solid is the image seen when looking straight down at the figure.

Draw the top view of the solid at the right by answering 1 and 2.

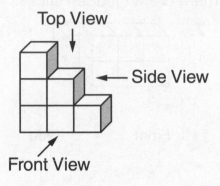

Top View

Side View

Front View

1. How many cubes can you see when you look straight down at the solid?

    _____

2. Color in squares on the grid to indicate the blocks seen from the top view.

The front view is the image seen when looking straight at the cubes.

Draw the front view of the solid above by answering 3 and 4.

3. How many cubes can you see when you look straight at the solid?

    _____

4. Color in squares on the grid to indicate the blocks seen from the front view.

The side view is the image seen when looking at the side of the cubes.

Draw the side view of the solid above by answering 5 and 6.

5. How many cubes can you see when you look at the solid from the side?

    _____

6. Color in squares on the grid to indicate the blocks seen from the side view.

 MDIS 2.0

Views of Solid Figures (continued)

Draw the front, right, and top views of each solid figure.
There are no hidden cubes.

7.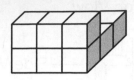

Front   Side   Top

8.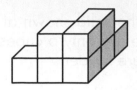

Front   Side   Top

9.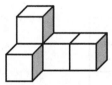

Top

Front

Side

10.

Top

Front

Side

11.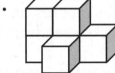

Top

Front

Side

12.   Reasoning If a cube is added to the top of the solid in
Exercise 11, what views would change? What view would
not change?

     MDIS 2.0

Name _____

Geometric Ideas

Materials crayons, markers, or colored pencils

A **plane** is an endless flat surface, such as this paper if it extended forever.

1. Name another real-world object which could represent a plane. _____

Use the diagram at the right to answer 2 to 8.

A **point** is an exact location in space.

2. Draw a circle around point *D* in orange.

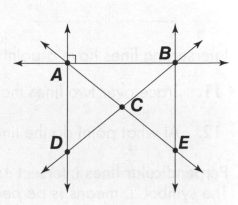

A **line** is a straight path of points that goes on forever in two directions.

3. Trace over line *AD* in blue.

Line *AD* is written $\overleftrightarrow{AD}$.

A **line segment** is a part of a line with two endpoints.

4. Trace over line segment *CD* in red. Be sure to stop at point *C* and point *D*.

Line segment *CD* is written $\overline{CD}$.

A **ray** is a part of a line with one endpoint.

5. Trace over ray *AB* in green. Ray *AB* is written $\overrightarrow{AB}$.

6. What point is the endpoint in ray *AB*? _____

An **angle** is formed by two rays with the same endpoint.

7. Trace over angle *ACB* in brown. Angle *ACB* is written ∠*ACB*.

The common endpoint of the rays is called the **vertex** of the angle.

8. Which point is the vertex of ∠*ACB*? _____

MDIS 2.0

Name _____

Geometric Ideas (continued)

Parallel lines never cross and stay the same distance apart. The symbol ∥ means *is parallel to.*

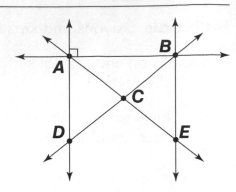

9. Trace over two lines that appear to be parallel, in purple.

10. Write the names of the parallel lines using the line symbol over the letters.

    _____ ∥ _____

Intersecting lines have a point in common.

11. Trace over two lines that intersect, in yellow.

12. At what point do the lines intersect?   _____

Perpendicular lines intersect and form a right angle. The symbol ⊥ means *is perpendicular to.*

13. Trace over two lines that are perpendicular, in orange.

14. Write the names of the perpendicular lines using the line symbol over the letters.   _____ ⊥ _____

Draw each of the following.

15. ray *HJ*

16. line segment *KL*

17. line *RS*

18. $\overleftrightarrow{TV}$ is parallel to $\overleftrightarrow{WX}$.

19. $\overline{EF}$ is perpendicular to $\overline{JK}$.

20. $\overleftrightarrow{YZ}$ intersects $\overleftrightarrow{AB}$.

MDIS 2.0

Name _____

Congruent Figures

Materials tracing paper and scissors

Two figures that have exactly the same size and shape are congruent.

1. Place a piece of paper over Figure A
   and trace the shape. Is the figure
   you drew congruent to Figure A? _____

Cut out the figure you traced and use it to
answer 2 to 10.

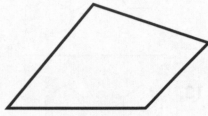

Figure A

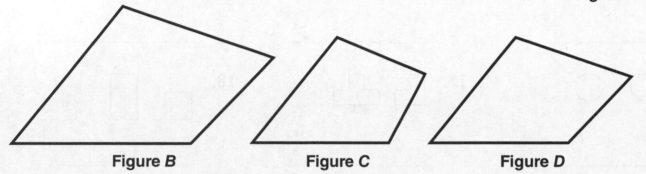

Figure B   **Figure C**   **Figure D**

2. Place the cutout on top of Figure B.
   Is Figure B the same size as Figure A?   _____

3. Is Figure B congruent to Figure A?   _____

4. Place the cutout on top of Figure C.
   Is Figure C the same shape as Figure A?   _____

5. Is Figure C congruent to Figure A?   _____

6. Place the cutout on top of Figure D.
   Is Figure D the same size as Figure A?   _____

7. Is Figure D the same shape as Figure A?   _____

8. Is Figure D congruent to Figure A?   _____

9. Circle the figure that is congruent to the figure at the right.

114 (student p. 1)   MDIS 2.0

Name _____

Congruent Figures (continued)

Tell if the two figures are congruent. Write Yes or No.

10.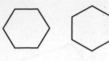

_____

11.

_____

12.

_____

13.

_____

14.

_____

15.

_____

16.

_____

17.

_____

18.

_____

19. Divide the isosceles triangle shown at the right into 2 congruent right triangles.

20. Divide the hexagon shown at the right into 6 congruent equilateral triangles.

21. Divide the rectangle shown at the right into 2 pairs of congruent triangles.

22. **Reasoning** Are the triangles at the right congruent? Why or why not?

 MDIS 2.0

Circles

Materials crayons, markers, or colored pencils

Use the figure at the right to answer 1 to 10.

A **circle** is the set of all points in a plane
that are the same distance from a point
called the **center**.

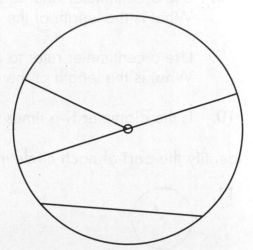

1. Color the point that is the center of
   the circle red.

A **radius** is any line that connects the
center of the circle to a point on the circle.

2. Color a radius of the circle blue.

3. **Reasoning** Will every radius that is drawn on
   the circle have same length? Explain your answer.

A **chord** is a line segment that connects any two points on a circle.
A chord may or may not go through the center of the circle.

4. Color a chord on the circle that does not include the center of the circle,
   green.

5. **Reasoning** Will every chord that is drawn on the circle have the same
   length? Explain your answer.

A **diameter** is a chord that goes through the center of the circle.

6. Color a diameter of the circle orange.

7. **Reasoning** Will every diameter that is drawn on the circle have the same
   length? Explain your answer.

 MDIS 2.0

Circles (continued)

The length of the diameter of a circle is two times the length of
the radius.

8. Use a centimeter ruler to measure the length of the radius.
What is the length of the radius? _____ cm

9. Use a centimeter ruler to measure the length of the diameter.
What is the length of the diameter? _____ cm

10. Is the diameter two times the length of the radius? _____

Identify the part of each circle indicated by the arrow.

11.

_____

12.

_____

13.

_____

14.

_____

15.

_____

16.

_____

Find the radius or diameter of each circle.

17.

radius:

_____

18.

diameter:

_____

19.

radius:

_____

20. The radius of a circle is 11 centimeters.
What is the diameter of the circle? _____

MDIS 2.0

Rotational Symmetry

Materials paper and scissors

If a figure can be turned less than
a full turn about a point and fit
back on itself, then the figure
has **rotational symmetry.**

All turns in this activity are assumed
to be clockwise. Find the types of
rotational symmetry for the figure
shown at the right by answering
1 to 11.

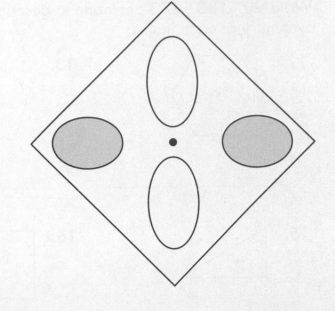

1. Place a piece of paper over the figure
    shown and trace it. Cut out the figure.

2. Place the cutout on top of the original figure, put your
    pencil on the dots to hold them in place, and rotate
    90 degrees clockwise or to the right around the point.

3. Does the cutout fit on top of the original figure?   _____

4. Does the figure have 90° rotational symmetry?   _____

5. Rotate the figure an additional 90 degrees clockwise
    around the point for a total of 180 degrees.

6. Does the cutout fit on top of the original figure?   _____

7. Does the figure have 180° rotational symmetry?   _____

8. Rotate the shape an additional 90 degrees clockwise
    around the point for a total of 270 degrees.

9. Does the cutout fit on top of the original figure?   _____

10. Does the figure have 270° rotational symmetry?   _____

11. What types of rotational symmetry does the figure have?   _____

Name _____

Rotational Symmetry (continued)

Write 90°, 180°, 270°, or none to describe the rotational
symmetry of each figure.

12.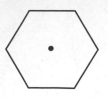

13.

14.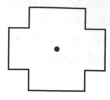

_____

15.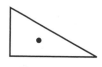

16.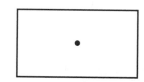

17.

_____

18.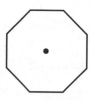

19.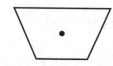

20.

_____

21.

22.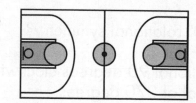

23.

_____

24. **Reasoning** Draw a figure with
90°, 180°, and 270° rotational
symmetry.

 MDIS 2.0

Name _____

Transformations

Materials paper, scissors, and markers.

Transformations do not change the size or shape of a figure. There are
three types of transformations: translation, reflection, and rotation.

Use a piece of paper to trace the house figure shown on the grid.
Then, cut it out. Answer 1 to 8.

A **translation** is a slide.

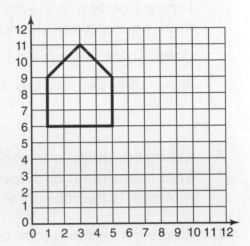

1. Place the cutout shape over the shape on
    the grid. What are the coordinates of each
    of the 5 vertices of the pentagon?

    _____

2. Slide the cutout shape 5 units to the right and
    trace around it. What are the coordinates of
    each of the 5 vertices after the translation?

    _____

3. Now slide the cutout shape 6 units down so that it is 5 units to the
    right and 6 units down from the original position and trace around
    it. What are the coordinates of each vertex after the translation?

    _____

A **reflection** is a flip or a mirror image.

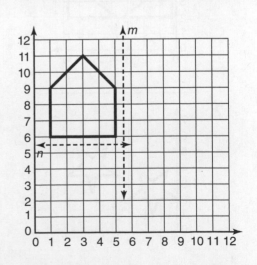

4. Place the cutout shape over the shape shown
    on the grid. Flip the house over line *m* and
    trace around it. The left side of the shape
    in the new position should be the same
    distance from the line as the right side
    was in the original position.

5. Place the cutout shape back in the
    original position. Flip the house over
    line *n* and trace around it.

  MDIS 2.0

Transformations (continued)

A **rotation** is a turn that moves a figure about a point. Each quarter turn is the same as a 90 degree rotation.

6. Place the cutout shape over the shape on the grid. Make a mark on the cutout at the same place as the dot. Turn the shape around the point clockwise so that the roof on the house is now pointing to the right or at 3 o'clock. The mark on the cutout should still be touching the point. Trace around the figure. This is a $\frac{1}{4}$ turn. How many degrees did the figure rotate?

_____

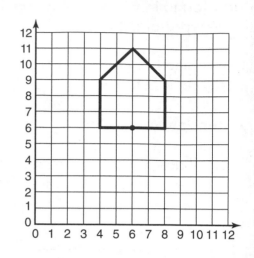

7. Rotate the shape a total of 180 degrees, or $\frac{1}{2}$ turn, from the original and trace around it. In what direction is the roof of the house now pointing? _____

8. Rotate the shape a total of 270 degrees, or $\frac{3}{8}$ turn, from the original and trace around it. In what direction is the roof pointing? _____

Tell whether the figures in each pair are related by a translation, a reflection, or a rotation.

9.

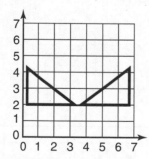

10.

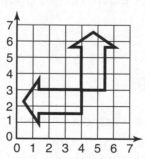

11.

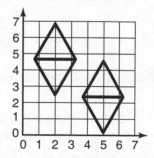

12.

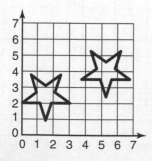

13.

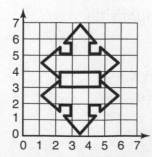

14.

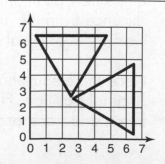

117 (student p. 2)

Measuring and Classifying Angles

Materials protractor, straightedge, and crayons, markers, or
colored pencils

A protractor can be used to measure and draw angles. Angles are measured in degrees.

Use a protractor to measure the angle shown by
answering 1 to 2.

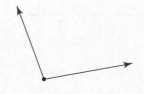

1. Place the protractor's center on the angle's
   vertex and place the 0° mark on one side
   of the angle.

2. Read the measure where the other side
   of the angle crosses the protractor.
   What is the measure of the angle?   _____

Use a protractor to draw an angle with a measure of 60°
by answering 3 to 5.

3. Draw $\overrightarrow{AB}$ by connecting the points shown
   with the endpoint of the ray at point A.

4. Place the protractor's center on point A.
   Place the protractor so the the 0° mark is
   lined up with $\overrightarrow{AB}$.

   $\overset{\bullet}{A}$ $\overset{\bullet}{B}$

5. Place a point at 60°. Label it C and draw $\overrightarrow{AC}$.

Use a protractor to measure the angles shown,
if necessary, to answer 6 to 9.

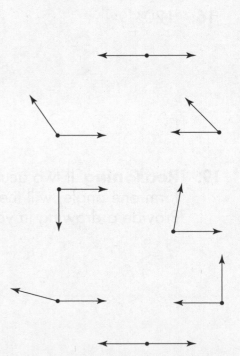

6. **Acute** angles have a measure between 0° and
   90°. Trace over the acute angles with blue.

7. **Right** angles have a measure of 90°. Trace
   over the right angles with red.

8. **Obtuse** angles have a measure between 90°
   and 180°. Trace over the obtuse angles with
   green.

9. **Straight** angles have a measure of 180°. Trace
   over the straight angles with orange.

         MDIS 2.0

Measuring and Classifying Angles (continued)

Classify each angle as acute, right, obtuse, or straight. Then measure the angle.

10.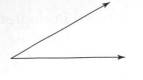

_____

_____

11.

_____

_____

12.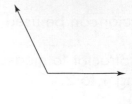

_____

_____

13.

_____

_____

14.

_____

_____

15.

_____

_____

Use a protractor to draw an angle with each measure.

16. 120°

17. 35°

18. 70°

19. Reasoning If two acute angles are placed next to each other to form one angle, will the result always be an obtuse angle? Explain. Provide a drawing in your explanation.

MDIS 2.0

Angle Pairs

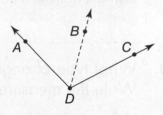

Adjacent angles are a pair of angles with a common vertex and a common side but no common interior points.

1. The picture at the right shows adjacent angles.
    Trace over the common side in the picture.

2. Name the two adjacent angles
    that share the side you traced.

    _____ and _____

Complementary angles are two angles whose measures add up to 90 degrees. **Supplementary angles** are two angles whose measures add up to 180 degrees.

3. One of the right angles in the diagram is formed
    by two smaller angles. These two angles are
    complementary. Name the complementary angles.

    _____ and _____

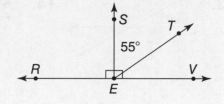

4. What is the measure of ∠SET?   _____

5. What is the measure of ∠TEV?   _____

6. Name an angle in the picture whose measure is 180°.   _____

7. Angle *REV* is divided into two angles, ∠RET and
    another one. Draw an arc on ∠RET. Name the
    other angle that makes up ∠REV. These two
    angles are supplementary.   _____

8. What angle is supplementary to ∠RES?   _____

When two lines intersect, angles are formed. Angles that are opposite one another with no common side are called **vertical angles**. Vertical angles have the same measure.

       MDIS 2.0

Name _____

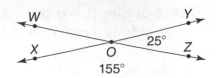

Angle Pairs (continued)

9. Draw an arc on ∠WOX. Name an angle
    in the picture that does not have a
    common side with ∠WOX.

    _____

10. What type of angles are ∠WOX and ∠YOZ?
    Write the measure of ∠WOX on the picture.   _____

11. What type of angles are ∠WOY and ∠YOZ?
    Write the measure of ∠WOY on the picture.   _____

12. What types of angles are ∠WOY and ∠XOZ?   _____

Find the measure of each angle labeled with a letter.

13.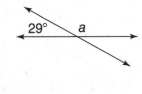

14.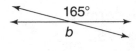

15.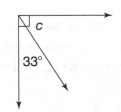

16.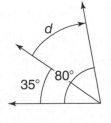

_____   _____   _____   _____

Find the measure of an angle that is complementary to an angle with each measure.

17. 84°   18. 4°   19. 16°   20. 72°

_____   _____   _____   _____

Find the measure of each angle by using the picture at the right.

21. ∠NOT   22. ∠PON

_____   _____

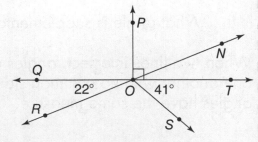

23. ∠POQ   24. ∠ROS

_____   _____

25. **Reasoning** What word can be used to describe two
    intersecting lines whose vertical angles are 90°?   _____

                   MDIS 2.0

Missing Angles in Triangles and Quadrilaterals

Materials index card and scissors

Find the relationship among angles in a triangle by answering 1 to 9.

1. Draw a triangle on an index card and
    cut it out.

2. Label each angle in the triangle with A,
    B, and C.

3. Cut out each corner of your triangle
    so that angles A, B, and C are
    separated from the triangle.

    ◄-------------•

4. Start with angle A. Place the vertex on the point shown above and
    one side of the angle on the dashed line. Trace around the angle.

5. Next place angle B's vertex on the point and one side of the angle so that
    it is sharing a side with angle A. Trace around the angle.

6. Next place angle C's vertex on the point and one side of the angle
    so that it is sharing a side with angle B. Trace around the angle.

7. **Reasoning** What do you notice about the angles of a triangle?

8. Compare your results with that of other students. Do the
    angles of the triangle have the same relationship?   _____

9. What is the sum of the measures of the three angles in
    any triangle?   _____

Find the relationship among angles in a quadrilateral by answering
10 to 16.

10. Draw a quadrilateral, that does not have any right angles, on an
    index card and cut it out.

11. Label each of the angles in the quadrilateral with A, B, C, and D.

Name _____

Missing Angles in Triangles and Quadrilaterals (continued)

12. Cut out each corner of your
quadrilateral so that angles *A, B, C,*
and *D* are separated from the
quadrilateral.

←-------------●

13. Place the vertex of each angle on the
point shown. Position the angles so
that they are adjacent and share a
common side.

14. **Reasoning** What do you notice about the angles of a quadrilateral?

15. Compare your results with that of other students. Do the
angles of their quadrilateral have the same relationship? _____

16. What is the sum of the measures of the four angles in
a quadrilateral? _____

Find the missing angle measures.

17.

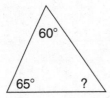

18.

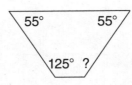

19.

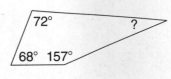

_____   _____   _____

20.

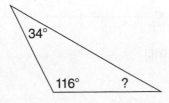

21.

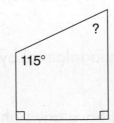

22.

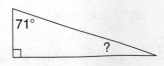

_____   _____   _____

         MDIS 2.0

Name _____

Measuring Length to $\frac{1}{2}$ and $\frac{1}{4}$ Inch

Materials inch ruler for each student, crayons or markers.

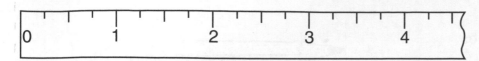

The distance between 0 and 1 on the ruler is one inch. So is the space between 1 and 2, 2 and 3, and so on.

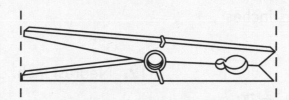

1. Line up the left edge of the clothespin with the 0 mark on the ruler. Is the clothespin's length closer to the 2 inch mark or the 3 inch mark?   _____

2. What is the clothespin's length to the nearest inch?   _____

3. How many spaces are between 0 and 1 on the ruler above?   _____

4. So each space is what part of an inch? _____

5. Color the marks in the ruler above that are $\frac{1}{4}$ inch and $\frac{3}{4}$ inch from zero red. Then color the rest of the $\frac{1}{4}$ inch marks red including $1\frac{1}{4}$, $1\frac{3}{4}$, $2\frac{1}{4}$, $2\frac{3}{4}$, and so on. Color the mark that is $\frac{2}{4}$ or $\frac{1}{2}$ inch from zero blue. Then color the rest of the $\frac{1}{2}$ inch marks blue, including $1\frac{1}{2}$, $2\frac{1}{2}$, and so on.

6. What is the length of the clothespin to the nearest $\frac{1}{2}$ inch? _____

Measure the length of the cricket to the nearest inch, $\frac{1}{2}$ inch and $\frac{1}{4}$ inch.

7. nearest inch _____ inch

8. nearest $\frac{1}{2}$ inch _____ inches

9. nearest $\frac{1}{4}$ inch _____ inches

 MDIS 2.0

Name _____

Measuring Length to $\frac{1}{2}$ and $\frac{1}{4}$ Inch (continued)

Measure each object to the nearest inch, $\frac{1}{2}$ inch, and $\frac{1}{4}$ inch.

10. Nearest inch: _____ inches

11. Nearest $\frac{1}{2}$ inch: _____ inches

    Nearest $\frac{1}{4}$ inch: _____ inches

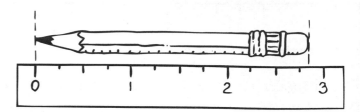

12. Nearest inch: _____ inches

13. Nearest $\frac{1}{2}$ inch: _____ inches

    Nearest $\frac{1}{4}$ inch: _____ inches

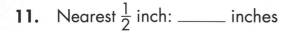

14. Nearest inch: _____ inch

15. Nearest $\frac{1}{2}$ inch: _____ inches

    Nearest $\frac{1}{4}$ inch: _____ inches

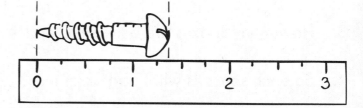

16. **Reasoning** Which gives the closest measurement, measuring to the nearest inch, $\frac{1}{2}$ inch, or $\frac{1}{4}$ inch? Explain.

 MDIS 2.0

Name _____

Using Customary Units of Length

A small paperclip is about 1 *inch* long.

A baseball bat is about 1 *yard* long.

A football is about 1 *foot* long.

Most people can walk a *mile* in about 15 minutes.

What is the best unit to measure each?

1. The length of your pencil _____

2. The length of the Mississippi River _____

3. The height of a desk _____

4. The length of your school _____

Answer 5 to 7 and use the table to find how many inches are in 4 feet.

5. 1 foot = _____ inches

6. To find how many inches are in 4 feet, multiply 4 × 12 inches.

   4 × 12 inches = _____ inches

7. How many inches are in 4 feet? _____

Customary Units of Length
1 foot (ft) = 12 inches
1 yard (yd) = 3 feet
1 yard = 36 inches
1 mile (mi) = 5,280 feet
1 mile = 1,760 yards

Answer 8 to 10 and use the table to find how many feet are in 5 yards, 2 feet.

8. 1 yard = _____ feet

9. How many feet are in 5 yards?   5 × 3 feet = _____ feet

10. How many feet are in 3 yards, 2 feet?   15 feet + 2 feet = _____ feet

                     MDIS 2.0

Using Customary Units of Length (continued)

Which unit would you use to measure each item?
Write *inch*, *foot*, *yard*, or *mile*.

11. The length of a gerbil

_____

12. The length of a football field

_____

13. The height of a door

_____

14. The distance to the sun

_____

Circle the better estimate.

15. The distance you travel on
an airplane

560 yards   or   560 miles

16. The height of a full grown
adult giraffe

6 feet   or   6 yards

17. The length of a bar of soap

3 inches   or   7 inches

18. The length of your bed

7 feet   or   7 yards

Find each missing number.

19. 2 yards = _____ feet

20. 3 feet = _____ inches

21. 4 yards = _____ inches

22. 3 yards, 2 feet = _____ feet

23. 1 foot, 9 inches = _____ inches

24. 2 yards, 2 feet = _____ inches

25. **Reasoning** What unit would you use to measure the length
of an earthworm? Explain why your choice is the best unit.

         MDIS 2.0

Name _____

Using Metric Units of Length

Materials centimeter ruler for each student

Your finger is about 1 centimeter wide.

1. Use the width of your finger to estimate the length of the pencil.

   Estimate: _____ of my finger widths = about _____ centimeters

2. Line up the 0 mark on the ruler with the left edge of the pencil.

3. What is the length of the pencil
   to the nearest centimeter?   _____

   A dime is about 1 *millimeter* thick.

   ▬▬▬▬▬

   A door knob is about 1 *meter*
   above the floor.

   A new crayon is almost
   1 *decimeter* long.

   Most people can walk a
   kilometer in about 10 minutes.

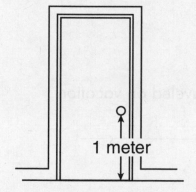

1 meter

What is the best unit to measure each?

4. the length of your finger   _____

5. the distance across your state   _____

6. the length of a lady bug   _____

123 (student p. 1)   MDIS 2.0

Name _____

Using Metric Units of Length (continued)

Answer 7 to 9 and use the table to find how many centimeters
are in 4 meters, 76 centimeters.

7. 1 meter = _____ centimeters

8. How many centimeters are
    in 4 meters?

    4 × 100 cm = _____ cm

9. How many centimeters are in
    4 meters, 76 centimeters?

    400 cm + 76 cm = _____ cm

Metric Units of Length	
1 centimeter (cm) =	10 millimeters
1 decimeter (dm) =	10 centimeters
1 meter (m) =	100 centimeters
1 kilometer (km) =	1,000 meters

Estimate the length of the spoon. Then measure to the
nearest centimeter.

10.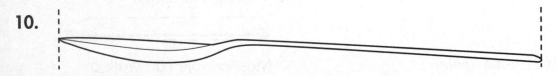

    _____

What unit would you use to measure each item?
Write *millimeter, centimeter, decimeter, meter,* or *kilometer.*

11. An adult's height

    _____

12. Distance traveled on vacation

    _____

Choose the best estimate.

13. Length of a car

    5 decimeters or 5 meters

14. Length of a calculator

    12 centimeters or 12 decimeters

Find each missing number.

15. 3 meters 18 centimeters = _____ centimeters

16. 6 meters 3 centimeters = _____ centimeters

123 (student p. 2)   MDIS 2.0

Using Customary Units of Capacity

Materials 6 stations each equipped with one set of the following: one cup, one pint, one quart, and one gallon measuring container labeled with its units; one of 6 different sized containers to be measured labeled A, B, C, D, E, and F; enough rice to fill the container at least one and a half times; a piece of paper taped into a funnel for containers with small openings

The **capacity** of a container is the amount the container can hold.

Go to each station. Find the row in the table which matches the letter on the container. Complete the table by doing the following.

Customary Units of Capacity	
1 pint (pt) = 2 cups (c)	
1 quart (qt) = 2 pints	
1 gallon (gal) = 4 quarts	

- Decide what unit to use to measure the lettered container.

- Estimate the capacity of the container.

- Then measure the capacity of the container by filling the cup, pint, quart, or gallon container with rice and pouring it into the container until that container is full.

	Container	Best Unit	Estimate	Capacity
1.	A			
2.	B			
3.	C			
4.	D			
5.	E			
6.	F			

124 (student p. 1)

Name _____

Using Customary Units of Capacity (continued)

What unit would you use to measure the capacity of each item?
Write *cup*, *pint*, *quart*, or *gallon*.

7. A pond

_____

8. A watering can

_____

9. A juice box

_____

10. A kitchen sink

_____

11. A coffee mug

_____

12. A pitcher of water

_____

13.

1 pt or 1 gal

14.

1 c or 1 qt

15.

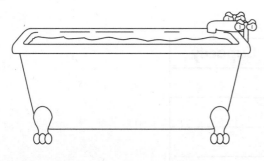

25 c or 25 gal

16.

2 c or 2 qt

17. **Reasoning** Martin bought a pint of grape juice. Franco bought a gallon of orange juice. Seth bought a quart of apple juice. List the type of juice in order from least to greatest capacities.

_____

18. **Reasoning** Romona is making spaghetti. Explain why the better estimate for the amount of water boiling in the pot is 2 quarts and not 2 cups.

124 (student p. 2) MDIS 2.0

Name _____

Using Metric Units of Capacity

A water bottle holds about 1 liter.

A medicine dropper holds about 1 milliliter.

1 liter

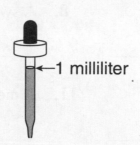

←—1 milliliter

Garrison wants to find out how much a small bottle of perfume holds. Decide whether he should measure the amount in liters or milliliters by answering 1 and 2.

Metric Units of Capacity
1 liter (L) = 1,000 milliliters (mL)

1. Would the perfume bottle hold more than a medicine dropper?

   _____

2. Would the perfume bottle hold more than a water bottle?

   _____

   Since the perfume bottle holds less than 1 liter, it should be measured in milliliters.

Decide whether 2 milliliters or 2 liters is a better estimate for the amount of soup the bowl holds by answering 3 to 5.

3. Would 2 medicine droppers fill the bowl? _____

4. Would 2 water bottles fill the bowl? _____

5. Which is better estimate? _____

6. **Reasoning** Explain why the better estimate for the amount of water a bucket holds is 8 liters and not 8 milliliters.

125 (student p. 1) MDIS 2.0

Name _____

Using Metric Units of Capacity (continued)

Choose a unit to measure the capacity of each item. Write *liters* or *milliliters*.

7. A can of soda

_____

8. A swimming pool

_____

9. A kitchen sink

_____

10. A birdbath

_____

11. A measuring spoon

_____

12. A soup bowl

_____

Circle the best estimate.

13.

4 L or 400 mL

14.

6 L or 650 mL

15.

7 L or 700 mL

16.

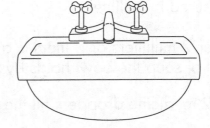

6 L or 60 mL

17.

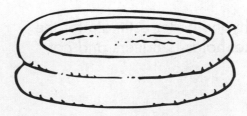

4 liters   1 liter   40 liters

          MDIS 2.0

Using Customary Units of Weight

The **weight** of an object is the measure of how heavy the object is.

A key weighs about 1 ounce.

A football weighs about 1 pound.

A bull weighs about 1 ton.

Lucy wants to find out how much her cat weighs. Decide whether she should use ounces, pounds, or tons by answering 1 to 3.

Customary Units of Weight
1 pound (lb) = 16 ounces (oz)
1 ton (T) = 2,000 pounds

1. Would the cat be heavier than a key? _____

2. Would the cat be heavier than a football? _____

3. Would the cat be heavier than a bull? _____

Since the cat would weigh more than a key, and more than a football, but less than a bull, it should be measured in pounds.

When measuring the weight of light objects, use ounces. When measuring the weight of heavier objects, use pounds. When measuring the weight of very heavy objects, like a bull, use tons.

Decide whether 4 pounds or 4 ounces is a better estimate for the weight of a carrot by answering 4 to 6.

4. Would a carrot feel as heavy as 4 footballs? _____

5. Would a carrot feel as heavy as 4 keys? _____

6. Which is a better estimate for the weight of a carrot, 4 ounces or 4 pounds? _____

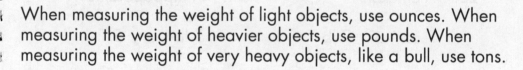

MDIS 2.0

Using Customary Units of Weight (continued)

Choose a unit to measure the weight of each item. Write ounces, pounds, or tons.

7. Eyeglasses

_____

8. An adult whale

_____

9. A dog

_____

10. A tomato

_____

11. An eraser

_____

12. A school bus

_____

13. A ship

_____

14. A guitar

_____

15. A desk

_____

16. A mouse

_____

17. A motor scooter

_____

18. A feather

_____

Circle the best estimate for the weight of each item.

19. The space shuttle

45 lb   or   45 T

20. A bowling ball

10 oz   or   10 lb

21. A slice of bread

1 oz   or   1 lb

22. A turkey

15 oz   or   15 lb

23. A chicken

7 oz   or   7 lb

24. A hippopotamus

5 lb   or   5 T

25. **Reasoning** Explain why the better estimate for the weight of a pencil is 1 ounce and not 1 pound.

26. **Reasoning** If you had a bag of apples that weighed a pound and a bag of marshmallows that weighed a pound, which bag would have more items in it? Explain.

  MDIS 2.0

Name _____

Using Metric Units of Mass

The amount of matter in an object is its **mass**.

A cantaloupe has
a mass of about
1 kilogram.

1 kilogram

A grape has
a mass of about
1 gram.

1 gram

Chi wants to find the mass of a bag of
potatoes. Decide whether he should
use grams or kilograms by answering
1 and 2.

Metric Units of Mass	
1 kilogram (kg)	= 1,000 grams (g)

1. Would the bag be heavier than
   a grape?   _____

2. Would the bag be heavier than
   a cantaloupe?   _____

Since the bag of potatoes has a mass greater than a grape, and
greater than a cantaloupe, it should be measured in kilograms.

When measuring the mass of lighter objects, use grams. When
measuring the mass of heavier objects, use kilograms.

Decide whether 300 kilograms or 300 grams is a better estimate
for the mass of a bag of pretzels by answering 3 to 5.

3. Would a bag of pretzels feel as heavy as
   300 cantaloupes?   _____

4. Would a bag of pretzels feel as heavy as
   300 grapes?   _____

5. Which is the better estimate for the mass of
   a bag of pretzels, 300 kilograms or 300 grams?   _____

127 (student p. 1)   MDIS 2.0

Using Metric Units of Mass (continued)

Choose a unit to measure the mass of each item. Write *grams* or *kilograms*.

6. car _____

7. pencil _____

8. calculator _____

9. dog _____

10. key _____

11. hairbrush _____

12. flowerpot _____

13. flower _____

Choose the better estimate.

14.

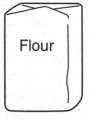

200 g   or   2 kg

15.

40 g   or   4 kg

16.

250 g   or   250 kg

17.

5 g   or   5 kg

18. **Reasoning** Why would you measure the mass of a goldfish in grams and not kilograms?

19. **Reasoning** Explain why the better estimate for the mass of a baby is 4 kilograms and not 4 grams.

 MDIS 2.0

Time to the Quarter Hour

Name _____

Use the clocks at the right to answer 1 to 6.

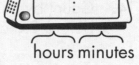

1. What two numbers is the hour hand between?

_____ and _____

2. Since the hour hand has not reached the 1, it is after 12:00. Write 12 for the hours in the digital clock.

hours minutes

3. What number is the minute hand on? _____

4. Each number on the clock represents 5 minutes after the hour. Count by 5s. How many minutes is it after 12? _____

5. Write 15 for the minutes in the digital clock.

The clock shows 12:15 or twelve fifteen.

6. Write 12:15 in two other ways.

15 minutes past _____;   quarter past _____

Use the clock at the right to answer 7 to 11.

7. What two numbers is the hour hand between?

_____ and _____

8. What is the hour? _____

9. What number is the minute hand on? _____

10. Count by 5s. How many minutes is it after the hour? _____

11. Write the time in three ways.

_____ : _____; _____ minutes past _____; _____ past _____

128 (student p. 1)   MDIS 2.0

Name _____

Time to the Quarter Hour (continued)

For Exercises 12 to 15, use the clock at the right.

12. What time is shown on the clock? _____ : _____

13. What hour is it about to be? _____

14. Count by 5s. How many minutes is it
    before 2 o'clock? _____

15. Write the time in two other ways.

    15 minutes to _____;   quarter to _____

Write the hour and then the minutes after the hour. Then circle the two correct times.

16.

hour _____

minutes _____

2:45	3:45	1:45
quarter to 2	15 minutes to 3	quarter past 2

17.

hour _____

minutes _____

4:15	6:15	5:15
quarter past 6	quarter past 5	15 minutes to 5

18.

hour _____

minutes _____

7:30	8:30	9:30
half past 8	quarter past 8	30 minutes past 9

19.

hour _____

minutes _____

11:45	11:15	12:45
quarter to 11	15 minutes to 11	quarter to 12

 MDIS 2.0

Name _____

Telling Time

Find the time on the clock by answering 1 to 8.

1. What two numbers is the hour hand between?

   _____ and _____

2. Since the hour hand has not reached the 6, it is after 5:00. Write 5 for the hours in the digital clock.

   hours minutes

3. It takes the minute hand 5 minutes to move from one number to the next. To find the minutes, first count by 5s from the 12 to the 7. Then count by 1s for each small mark after the 7.

4. How many minutes is it after 5? _____
   Write the minutes in the digital clock above.

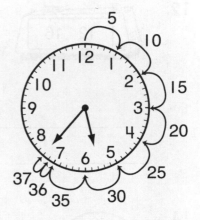

5. Write the time in three different ways.

   _____ : _____ ;

   _____ thirty-seven;

   _____ minutes past 5

6. To find how many minutes before the next hour, count the other way. Count by 5s from the 12 to the 8, then count by 1s for each small mark after the 8.

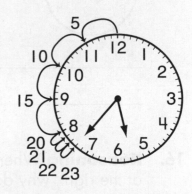

7. How many minutes is it before 6? _____

8. Write the time another way.

   _____ minutes to 6

9. Write the time shown on the clock at the right in two different ways.

   2 : 24

   _____ twenty-_____ ; _____ minutes past 2

129 (student p. 1)   MDIS 2.0

Name _____

Telling Time (continued)

Write the time shown on each clock in two ways.

10.

_____

_____

11.

8 : 53

_____

_____

12.

12 : 16

_____

_____

13.

_____

_____

14.

_____

_____

15.

_____

_____

16. **Reasoning** When finding the number of minutes on the clock
at the right, why do you first count by 5s and then by ones?

 MDIS 2.0

Units of Time

Benny spent 3 weeks at his cousin's house. Find how many days Benny spent at his cousin's by using the table and answering 1 to 3.

1. 1 week = _____ days

2. To find how many days are in 3 weeks, multiply 3 × 7 days.

    3 × 7 days = _____ days

3. How many days did Benny spend at his cousin's? _____ days

Relating Units of Time
1 week = 7 days
1 day = 24 hours
1 hour = 60 minutes

The talent show lasted 2 hours and 17 minutes. Find how many minutes the talent show lasted by using the table and answering 4 to 6.

4. 1 hour = _____ minutes

5. First, find the number of minutes in 2 hours. Then add the 17 minutes.

    2 × 60 minutes = _____ minutes

    120 minutes + 17 minutes = _____ minutes

6. How many minutes did the talent show last? _____ minutes

Cindy left her radio on for 4 days, 5 hours. Find how many hours Cindy's radio stayed on by using the table and answering 7 to 9.

7. 1 day = _____ hours

8. First find the number of hours in 4 days. Then add the 5 hours.

    4 × 24 hours = _____ hours

    96 hours + 5 hours = _____ hours

9. How many hours did Cindy's radio stay on? _____ hours

 MDIS 2.0

Name _____

Units of Time (continued)

Intervention
Lesson **130**

Find the missing numbers.

10. 6 hours = _____ minutes

11. 8 days = _____ hours

12. 9 weeks = _____ days

13. 5 hours = _____ minutes

14. 5 days, 3 hours = _____ hours

15. 1 hour, 2 minutes = _____ minutes

16. 6 weeks, 6 days = _____ days

17. 3 days, 16 hours = _____ hours

18. The first space flight when humans orbited the earth lasted 1 hour, 48 minutes. How many minutes did the flight last?

_____

19. The first space flight when humans orbited the moon lasted 6 days, 3 hours. How many hours did the mission last?

_____

20. It normally takes a duck egg 4 weeks, 2 days to hatch. How many days is 4 weeks, 2 days?

_____

21. It normally takes a pigeon egg 2 weeks, 4 days to hatch. How many days is 2 weeks, 4 days?

_____

22. **Reasoning** A chicken egg normally hatches in 21 days. A turkey egg normally hatches in 3 weeks, 5 days. How many more days does it normally take a turkey egg to hatch than a chicken egg? Explain how you solved.

23. Eddie ran a marathon in 4 hours and 7 minutes. His goal was to finish the race in less than 250 minutes. Did Eddie achieve his goal? Explain your reasoning.

MDIS 2.0

Elapsed Time

The party starts at 2:00 P.M. and ends at 4:45 P.M. How long is the party?

Start   **End**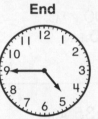

1. How many hours from 2:00 P.M. to 4:00 P.M.? _____ hours

2. How many minutes from 4:00 P.M. to 4:45 P.M.? _____ minutes

3. How long did the party last? _____ hours, _____ minutes

School starts at 8:20 A.M. and ends at 3:30 P.M. How long does school last?

Start   **End**

4. How many hours from 8:20 A.M. to 3:20 P.M.? _____ hours

5. How many minutes from 3:20 P.M. to 3:30 P.M.? _____ minutes

6. How long does school last? _____ hours, _____ minutes

Reasoning The flight lasted 3 hours 20 minutes. If the plane took off at 4:10 P.M., what time did it land?

7. What time is 3 hours after 4:10 P.M.? _____ P.M.

8. What time is 20 minutes after 7:10 P.M.? _____ P.M.

9. What time did the plane land? _____ P.M.

 MDIS 2.0

Elapsed Time (continued)

Find the elapsed time.

10. Start Time: 1:00 P.M.
End Time: 8:00 P.M.

_____

11. Start Time: 7:00 A.M.
End Time: 10:35 A.M.

_____

12. Start Time: 11:35 A.M.
End Time: 3:50 P.M.

_____

13. Start Time: 6:10 P.M.
End Time: 12:25 A.M.

_____

14. Start Time: 2:00 P.M.
End Time: 6:05 P.M.

_____

15. Start Time: 9:20 A.M.
End Time: 2:40 P.M.

_____

16. Start Time: 4:35 P.M.
End Time: 5:15 P.M.

_____

17. Start Time: 8:15 A.M.
End Time: 2:55 A.M.

_____

18. Reasoning The baseball game started at 3:00 P.M. It lasted 2 hours and 45 minutes. What time did the baseball game end?

_____

19. Reasoning Erin got home from the soccer match at 5:20 P.M. She went to bed 3 hours and 45 minutes later. What time did she go to bed?

_____

20. Reasoning The rainstorm began at 1:15 P.M. Marco's class came in from recess 25 minutes earlier. What time did the class come in from recess?

_____

21. Reasoning What is 30 minutes before 12:25 P.M.?

_____

 MDIS 2.0

Converting Customary Units of Length

Mayla bought 6 yards of ribbon. How many feet of ribbon did she buy?

Answer 1 to 4 to change 6 yards to feet.

To change larger units to smaller units, multiply. To change smaller units to larger units, divide.

Customary Units of Length	
1 foot (ft) = 12 inches (in.)	
1 yard (yd) = 36 (in.)	
1 yard (yd) = 3 feet (ft)	
1 mile (mi) = 5,280 feet (ft)	
1 mile (mi) = 1,760 yards (yd)	

1. 1 yard = _____ feet

2. Do you need to multiply or divide to change from yards to feet? _____

3. What is 6 × 3 feet? _____ feet

4. How many feet of ribbon did Mayla buy? _____

Deidra bought 60 inches of ribbon. How many feet of ribbon did she buy? Change 60 inches to feet by answering 5 to 8.

5. 1 foot = _____ inches

6. Do you need to multiply or divide to change from feet to inches? _____

7. What is 60 ÷ 12? _____

8. How many feet of ribbon did Deidra buy? _____

Troy ran 4 miles. How many yards did he run? Change 4 miles to yards by answering 9 to 11.

9. 1 mile = _____ yards

10. Do you need to multiply or divide to change from miles to yards? _____

11. 4 miles = _____ yards

12. How many yards did Troy run? _____

   MDIS 2.0

Converting Customary Units of Length (continued)

Find each missing number.

13. 1 yd = _____ ft   **14.** 72 in. = _____ ft   **15.** 3 mi = _____ ft

16. 5,280 ft = _____ mi   **17.** 5 mi = _____ yd   **18.** 4 yd = _____ ft

19. 48 in. = _____ ft   **20.** 1 yd = _____ in.   **21.** 6 mi = _____ ft

22. 5 yd = _____ ft   **23.** 3 mi = _____ yd   **24.** 2 ft = _____ in.

25. 21 ft = _____ yd   **26.** 3 yd = _____ in.   **27.** 4 yd = _____ in.

For Exercises 28 to 32 use the information in the table.

28. How many inches did Speedy crawl?

_____ inches

29. How many inches did Pokey crawl?

_____ inches

30. How many inches did Pickles crawl?

_____ inches

31. Reasoning Which turtle crawled the greatest distance? _____

32. Reasoning Which turtle crawled the least distance? _____

33. Reasoning Explain how you could use addition to find how many yards are in 72 inches.

Turtle Crawl Results

Turtle	Distance
Snapper	38 inches
Speedy	3 feet
Pokey	2 yards
Pickles	4 feet

MDIS 2.0

Name _____

Converting Customary Units of Capacity

The bread recipe calls for
2 cups of milk. How many
fluid ounces (fl oz) is that?
Change 2 cups to fluid ounces
by answering 1 to 3.

To change larger units to
smaller units, multiply.
To change smaller units
to larger units, divide.

Customary Units of Capacity	
1 tablespoon (tbsp) = 3 teaspoons (tsp)	
1 cup (c) = 8 fluid ounces (fl oz)	
1 pint (pt) = 2 cups (c)	
1 quart (qt) = 2 pints (pt)	
1 gallon (gal) = 4 quarts (qt)	

1. 1 cup = _____ fluid ounces

2. Do you need to multiply or divide to change from cups to fluid ounces? _____

3. What is 2 × 8 fluid ounces? _____ fluid ounces

4. How many fluid ounces of milk is 2 cups? _____

Change 18 teaspoons to tablespoons by answering 5 to 8.

5. 1 tablespoon = _____ teaspoons

6. Do you need to multiply or divide to change from teaspoons to tablespoons? _____

7. What is 18 ÷ 3? _____

8. 18 tablespoon = _____ teaspoons

Javier made 5 quarts of punch. How many pints did he make?
Change 5 quarts to pints by answering 9 to 12.

9. 1 quart = _____ pints

10. Do you need to multiply or divide to change from quarts to pints? _____

11. 5 quarts = _____ pints

12. How many pints of punch did Javier make? _____

 MDIS 2.0

Converting Customary Units of Capacity (continued)

Find each missing number.

13. 40 fl oz = _____ c
14. 3 gal = _____ qt
15. 15 tsp = _____ tbsp

16. 4 qt = _____ pt
17. 12 pt = _____ qt
18. 8 c = _____ fl oz

19. 3 tbsp = _____ tsp
20. 18 c = _____ pt
21. 14 gal = _____ qt

22. 24 fl oz = _____ c
23. 16 qt = _____ pt
24. 32 qt = _____ gal

25. 3 pt = _____ c
26. 8 qt = _____ gal
27. 4 c = _____ pt

Lee has the supplies listed in the table to use in his science fair
project. Use the table for Exercises 28 to 32.

28. How many cups of orange
juice does Lee have? _____ cups

29. How many cups of milk
does Lee have? _____ cups

30. How many cups of water
does Lee have? _____ cups

Science Project Supplies

Liquid	Amount
Orange Juice	32 fl oz
Milk	1 pt
Vinegar	3 c
Water	3 pt

31. Reasoning Which liquid does Lee have the most of? _____

32. Reasoning Which liquid does Lee have the least of? _____

33. Reasoning Lee also needs 4 tablespoons of baking
soda, but he can only find a teaspoon to measure with.
How many teaspoons of baking soda does he need? _____

34. Reasoning Explain how to convert 6 pints to quarts.

133 (student p. 2)   MDIS 2.0

Converting Customary Units of Weight

An average size ostrich egg weighs 3 pounds. How many ounces does an average size ostrich egg weigh?

Change 3 pounds to ounces by answering 1 to 4.

To change larger units to smaller units, multiply. To change smaller units to larger units, divide.

Customary Units of Weight	
1 pound (lb) = 16 ounces (oz)	
1 ton (T) = 2,000 pounds (lb)	

1. 1 pound = _____ ounces

2. Do you need to multiply or divide to change from pounds to ounces?   _____

3. What is 3 × 16 ounces? _____ ounces

4. How many ounces does an average size ostrich egg weigh? _____

An African elephant can weigh up to 22,000 pounds. How many tons can an African elephant weigh? Change 22,000 pounds to tons by answering 5 to 8.

5. 1 ton = _____ pounds

6. Do you need to multiply or divide to change from pounds to tons?   _____

7. What is 22,000 ÷ 2,000? Hint: Think 22 ÷ 2. _____

8. How many tons can an African elephant weigh? _____

An Asian elephant can grow to a little more than 5 tons. How many pounds can the Asian elephant weigh? Change 5 tons to pounds by answering 9 to 12.

9. 1 ton = _____ pounds

10. Do you need to multiply or divide to change from tons to pounds?   _____

 MDIS 2.0

Converting Customary Units of Weight (continued)

11. 5 tons = _____ pounds

12. How many pounds can an Asian elephant weigh? _____

Find each missing number.

13. 8 lb = _____ oz   **14.** 12 T = _____ lb   **15.** 48 oz = _____ lb

16. 24,000 lb = _____ T **17.** 80 oz = _____ lb   **18.** 22 T = _____ lb

19. 64 oz = _____ lb   **20.** 4,000 lb = _____ T **21.** 22 lb = _____ oz

22. 14,000 lb = _____ T **23.** 160 oz = _____ lb   **24.** 10 T = _____ lb

25. 4 T = _____ lb   **26.** 32 oz = _____ lb   **27.** 16,000 lb = _____ T

For Exercises 28 to 32, use the information in the table.

28. How many pounds of
carrots were shipped? _____ pounds

29. How many pounds of
peas were shipped? _____ pounds

30. **Reasoning** Which vegetable shipment
was the heaviest?

_____

31. **Reasoning** Which vegetable shipment was the lightest? _____

32. **Reasoning** Five tons of corn were shipped. Explain how to
find how many more pounds of potatoes than corn were shipped.

Vegetable Shipments

Vegetable	Amount
Carrots	4 T
Celery	12,000 lb
Peas	2 T
Potatoes	16,000 lb

 MDIS 2.0

Converting Metric Units

The table shows how metric units are related. Every unit is 10 times greater than the next smaller unit. Abbreviations are shown for the most commonly used units.

÷ 10   ÷ 10   ÷ 10   ÷ 10   ÷ 10   ÷ 10

kilometer (km)	hectometer	dekameter	meter (m)	decimeter	centimeter (cm)	millimeter (mm)
kiloliter	hectoliter	dekaliter	liter (L)	deciliter	centiliter	milliliter (mL)
kilogram (kg)	hectogram	dekagram	gram (g)	decigram	centigram	milligram (mg)

× 10   × 10   × 10   × 10   × 10   × 10

To change from one metric unit to another, move the decimal point to the right or to the left to multiply or divide by 10, 100, or 1,000.

The length of a sheet of paper is 27.9 centimeters. Convert 27.9 cm to millimeters by answering 1 to 3.

1. To move from centimeters to millimeters in the table, do you move right or left? _____

2. How many jumps are there between centimeters and millimeters in the table? _____

   Move the decimal one place to the right to convert from centimeters to millimeters. This is the same as multiplying by 10.

3. What is the length of the paper in millimeters? _____mm

Convert 27.9 cm to meters by answering 4 to 6.

4. To move from centimeters to meters in the table, do you move right or left? _____

   135 (student p. 1)   MDIS 2.0

Name _____

Converting Metric Units (continued)

5. How many jumps are there between centimeters and meters in the table? _____

   Move the decimal two places to the left to convert from centimeters to meters. This is the same as dividing by 100.

6. What is the length of the paper in meters? _____ m

Tell the direction and number of jumps in the table for each conversion. Then convert.

7. 742 cm to meters

   _____ jumps _____

   _____ m

8. 12.4 kg to g

   _____ jumps _____

   _____ g

9. 0.62 L to mL

   _____ jumps _____

   _____ mL

Write the missing numbers.

10. 150 mg = _____ g

11. 2,600 m = _____ km

12. 0.4 L = _____ mL

13. 300 mL = _____ L

14. 4 kg = _____ mg

15. 2.6 m = _____ mm

16. 2,670 mg = _____ g

17. 34 cm = _____ mm

18. 16 L = _____ mL

For Exercises 19 to 21 use the table at the right.

19. What is the height of the Petronas Towers in centimeters?

   _____

20. What is the height of the CN Tower in meters?

   _____

21. What is the height of the John Hancock Center in km?

   _____

Building	Height
John Hancock Center	344 m
Petronas Towers	452 m
Sears Tower	44,200 cm
CN Tower	553,000 mm

22. **Reasoning** Which is shorter, 15 centimeters or 140 millimeters? Explain.

 MDIS 2.0

Converting Between Measurement Systems

The table shows the relationships between customary and metric units. Only the equivalent for inches and centimeters is exact. All other equivalents are approximate. The symbol ≈ means "approximately equal to."

A standard CD has a diameter of 4.75 inches. How many centimeters is the diameter of the CD?

Convert 4.75 inches to centimeters by answering 1 to 4.

1. How many centimeters equal one inch? _____

To change larger units to smaller units multiply.
To change smaller units to larger units, divide.

2. Do you need to multiply or divide to change from inches to centimeters? _____

3. What is 4.75×2.54 to the nearest tenth? _____

4. How many centimeters is the diameter of the CD? _____cm

The average golden retriever weighs 65 pounds. What is the approximate mass in kilograms of an average golden retriever?

Convert 65 pounds to kilograms by answering 5 to 8.

5. According to the table, how many pounds equal about one kilogram? _____

6. Do you need to multiply or divide to change from pounds to kilograms? _____

7. What is $65 \div 2.2$ rounded to the nearest tenth? _____

8. What is the approximate mass in kilograms of an average golden retriever? _____kg

---

**Customary and Metric
Unit Equivalent**

Length
1 in. = 2.54 cm
1 m ≈ 39.97 in.
1 mi ≈ 1.61 km

Weight and Mass
1 oz ≈ 28.35 g
1 kg ≈ 2.2 lb
1 metric ton (t) ≈ 1.102 tons (T)

Capacity
1 L ≈ 1.06 qt
1 gal ≈ 3.79 L

 MDIS 2.0

Name _____

Converting Between Measurement Systems (continued)

Complete. Round to the nearest tenth, if necessary.

9. 3.8 m ≈ ■ in.

_____

10. 50 g ≈ ■ oz

_____

11. 3 L ≈ ■ gal

_____

12. 44 in. ≈ ■ cm

_____

13. 2.5 t ≈ ■ T

_____

14. $3\frac{1}{2}$ kg ≈ ■ lb

_____

15. $5\frac{1}{4}$ qt ≈ ■ L

_____

16. 100 km ≈ ■ mi

_____

17. 10 cm ≈ ■ in.

_____

18. 2 cm ≈ ■ in.

_____

19. 2.4 t ≈ ■ T

_____

20. $8\frac{2}{3}$ m ≈ ■ yd

_____

21. $3\frac{1}{2}$ yd ≈ ■ m

_____

22. 500 lb ≈ ■ kg

_____

23. 11 in. ≈ ■ m

_____

24. Rewrite the materials list at the right using meters for
fabric, inches for thread, and kilograms for stuffing.
Write your conversions to the nearest tenth below:

fabric: _____ m   thread: _____ in.   stuffing: _____ kg.

Materials List
$1\frac{1}{2}$ yd fabric
65 cm thread
$1\frac{3}{4}$ lb stuffing

25. **Reasoning** A necklace measures $16\frac{1}{2}$ inches.

About how many centimeters is this to the nearest tenth? _____

 MDIS 2.0

Name _____

Units of Measure and Precision

Materials inch and centimeter rulers, rectangle measuring
$3\frac{5}{16}$ inches by $\frac{7}{8}$ inches for each student, pair, or group

The smaller the units on the scale of a measuring device, the more precise the measurement.

Explore precision by answering 1 to 12.

1. What are the dimensions of the cut out
   rectangle to the nearest inch?   _____

2. Draw a rectangle with the dimensions found in item 1.

3. What are the dimensions of the cut out
   rectangle to the nearest eighth inch?   _____

4. Draw a rectangle with the dimensions found in item 3.

5. Which of the rectangles you drew is closest in size
   to the cut out rectangle?   _____

6. Which unit is more precise, inch or eighth inch? _____

7. What are the dimensions of the cut out
   rectangle to the nearest centimeter?   _____

8. Draw a rectangle with the dimensions found in item 7.

9. What are the dimensions of the cut out
   rectangle to the nearest millimeter?   _____

10. Draw a rectangle with the dimensions found in item 9.

                    MDIS 2.0

Units of Measure and Precision (continued)

11. Which of the last two rectangles you drew is closest
in size to the cut out rectangle?   _____

12. Which unit is more precise, centimeter or millimeter?   _____

13. Reasoning Which unit is more precise,
eighth inch or millimeter?   _____

Find the length of the crayon to each unit.

14. whole inch _____   **15.** quarter inch _____   **16.** eighth inch _____

17. sixteenth inch _____   **18.** centimeter _____   **19.** millimeter _____

20. Which measure of the crayon is the most precise?   _____

Measure each line segment to the nearest $\frac{1}{8}$ inch and nearest centimeter.

21. _____   **22.** _____

Measure each line segment to the nearest $\frac{1}{16}$ inch and nearest millimeter.

23. _____   **24.** _____

Circle the more precise measure in each.

25. 4 km or 2 mi   **26.** 2 gal or 8 L   **27.** 3 in. or 4 cm

More Units of Time

Natalia, one of the finalists at a dance marathon, danced 1,740 minutes. Tony, the other finalist, danced 28 hours and 20 minutes. Which finalist danced the longest?

Solve by answering 1 to 6.

To change a smaller unit to a larger unit, divide. To change a larger unit to a smaller unit, multiply.

Units of Time
1 minute = 60 seconds
1 hour = 60 minutes
1 day = 24 hours
1 week = 7 days
1 month = about 4 weeks
1 year = 52 weeks
1 year = 12 months
1 year = 365 days
1 leap year = 366 days
1 decade = 10 years
1 century = 100 years
1 millennium = 1,000 years

1. How many minutes
   are in an hour? _____

2. Do you need to multiply
   or divide to change
   from minutes to hours? _____

3. What is 1,740 ÷ 60? _____

4. How many hours equal
   1,740 minutes? _____

5. Compare. Write >, <, or =.

   1,740 min ◯ 28 h 20 min

6. Which finalist danced the longest? _____

Fred is two years and ten days older than Ron. Alfonzo is 745 days older than Ron. Who is older, Fred or Alfonzo?

Solve by answering 7 to 12.

7. How many days are in a year? _____

8. Do you need to multiply or divide to change years to days? _____

9. What is (2 × 365) + 10? _____

10. How many days are two years and ten days? _____

     MDIS 2.0

More Units of Time (continued)

---

11. Compare. Write >, <, or =.   2 years 10 days ◯ 745 days

12. Who is older, Fred or Alfonzo?   _____

13. **Reasoning** Find the missing numbers.

75 minutes = _____ hour, _____ minutes

Compare. Write >, <, or =.

14. 2 minutes ◯ 126 seconds

15. 4 weeks ◯ 28 days

16. 2 weeks and 3 days ◯ 16 days

17. 50 weeks ◯ 350 days

18. 50 hours ◯ 2 days

19. 208 minutes ◯ 4 hours

20. 2 decades ◯ 34 years

21. 28 months ◯ 2 years

22. 23 weeks ◯ 161 days

23. 6 hours ◯ 150 minutes

Find each missing number.

24. 420 seconds = _____ minutes

25. 156 weeks = _____ years

26. 105 days = _____ weeks

27. 3 hours = _____ seconds

28. **Reasoning** Jerome slept 8 hours and 35 minutes on Tuesday night while Manuel slept 525 minutes. Who slept longer? Explain how you solved.

   MDIS 2.0

More Elapsed Time

Elapsed time is the amount of time that passes between the beginning and the end of an event.

Simone's school starts at 8:40 A.M. and ends at 3:45 P.M. How much time does Simone spend at school?

Find the elapsed time that Simone is at school by answering 1 to 7.

1. How much time passes from 8:40 to 9:00? _____

2. How much time passes from 9:00 to 12:00? _____

3. How much time passes from 12:00 to 3:00? _____

4. How much time passes from 3:00 to 3:45? _____

5. What is 20 minutes + 3 hours + 3 hours + 45 minutes? _____

6. What is 65 minutes in hours and minutes? _____

7. How much time does Simone spend at school? _____

After school Simone spends 20 minutes walking home and she has 30 minutes before she must leave for soccer practice. What time must she leave for soccer practice?

Find the end time by answering 8 to 10.

8. School ends at 3:45 P.M. If Simone spends 20 minutes walking home, what time does she arrive at home? _____

 MDIS 2.0

Name _____

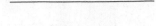

More Elapsed Time (continued)

9. Simone must leave for practice 30 minutes later.
   What time is it 30 minutes after 4:05? _____

10. What time must Simone leave for soccer practice? _____

11. Start: 3:05 A.M.
    Finish: 5:37 A.M.

12. Start: 10:45 A.M.
    Finish: 3:07 P.M.

13. Start: 4:58 P.M.
    Finish: 6:56 P.M.

_____   _____   _____

Write the time each clock will show in 38 minutes.

14.

15.

_____   _____

Write the time each clock will show in 3 hours and 35 minutes

16.

17.

_____   _____

Find each start or finish time.

18. Start: 2:24 P.M.

    Elapsed time:
    3 hours and 32 minutes

    Finish: _____

19. Start: _____

    Elapsed time:
    55 minutes

    Finish: 11:30 A.M.

20. A theater started a movie promptly at 6:30 P.M. If the
    movie finished at 8:22 P.M., how long was the movie? _____

         MDIS 2.0

Elapsed Time in Other Units

Salvador went to bed at 10:40 P.M. and woke up at a quarter to 8 the next morning. How many hours did Salvador sleep?

One way to find the elapsed time is with a number line.

Find the elapsed time by answering 1 to 6.

Elapsed Time

10:00   12:00   8:00
P.M.   A.M.   A.M.

1. Label each of the tick marks on the number line.

2. Plot and label a point on the number line that represents 10:40 P.M.

3. What time is a quarter to 8 in the morning? _____

4. Make jumps of length one hour on the number line, until you get close to 7:45, without going past it. How many jumps did you make? _____

5. Draw a small jump to 7:45 A.M.
   How much time is represented by all the jumps?   ____ h ____ min

6. How many hours did Salvador sleep?   ____ h ____ min

Another way to find elapsed time is to subtract.
End Time − Start Time = Elapsed Time

Find the elapsed time another way by answering 7 to 14.

$$11 \text{ h } \boxed{} \text{ min}$$

7. Subtract to find the elapsed time before midnight.
   12 hours is the same as 11 hours and how many minutes?

$$\begin{array}{r} \cancel{12 \text{ h } 00 \text{ min}} \\ - 10 \text{ h } 40 \text{ min} \\ \hline \boxed{} \end{array}$$

   12 h = 11 h _____ min
   Rename 12 hours 00 minutes at the right.

8. Subtract the minutes and record at the right.   60 min − 40 min = _____ min

9. Subtract the hours and record at the right.   11 h − 10 h = ____ h

10. How long did Salvador sleep before midnight?   ____ h ____ min

11. How long did Salvador sleep after midnight?   ____ h ____ min

140 (student p. 1)   MDIS 2.0

Elapsed Time in Other Units (continued)

12. Add the elapsed time before midnight to the elapsed time after midnight to find the total elapsed time. Record at the right.

1 h 20 min
+ 7 h 45 min
_____

20 min + 45 min = _____ min   1 h + 7 h = _____ h

13. Rename 8 hours 65 minutes.

65 minutes = ____ h _____ min   8 hours 65 minutes = ____ h _____ min

14. How many hours did Salvador sleep?   ____ h _____ min

Find each elapsed time.

15. 9:15 A.M. to 4:05 P.M.   **16.** Quarter to 8 in the evening to 2:30 A.M.

_____   _____

17. 1:26 P.M. to 5:56 A.M.   **18.** Quarter after 12 noon to 9:30 P.M.

_____   _____

Find each start or end time.

19. Start: 10:24 P.M.   **20.** Start: _____

Elapsed time: 3 h and 41 min   Elapsed time: 12 h 55 min

Finish: _____   Finish: 4:30 A.M.

Add or subtract.

21.   6 h 20 min
      − 3 h 40 min

22.   3 h 38 min
      + 6 h 47 min

23.   2 h 39 min
      +   56 min

24.   5 h 10 min
      − 2 h 55 min

25.   5 h 24 min
      + 3 h 41 min

26.   1 h 35 min
      −   56 min

27. Reasoning An airplane takes off at 11:50 P.M. and lands at 8:12 A.M. How long was the plane in the air?   _____

140 (student p. 2)   MDIS 2.0

Perimeter

Materials crayons or markers, centimeter ruler for each student.

Find the perimeter of the figure at the right by answering
1 to 3. **Perimeter** is the distance around a figure. Each
space between lines equals 1 unit.

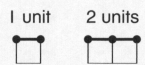

1 unit   2 units

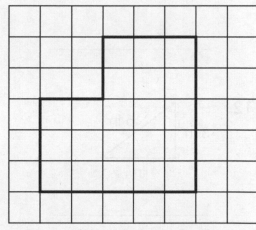

scale: |—| = 1 unit

1. Trace the figure with a crayon or marker. Count
    the number of spaces as you trace.

2. How many spaces did you trace? _____

3. What is the perimeter of the figure? _____ units

You can also find the perimeter by adding
the lengths of the sides.

Find the perimeter of the figure to the right
by answering 4 to 6.

4. How many sides
    does this figure have? _____

5. Trace over the sides as you count
    and record the length of each side.

scale: •—• = 1 meter

_____ + _____ + _____ + _____ + _____ + _____ = _____

6. What is the perimeter of the figure? _____ meters

Find the perimeter of the rectangle by answering 7 to 8.

Opposite sides of a rectangle have equal lengths.

7. Record the length of the sides. Find the sum.

    $10 + 3 +$ _____ $+$ _____ $=$ _____

8. What is the perimeter of the rectangle? _____ cm

10 cm

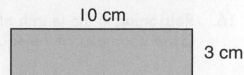

3 cm

141 (student p. 1)   MDIS 2.0

Perimeter (continued)

9. **Reasoning** Use a ruler to measure each side of the figure in inches. What is the perimeter of the figure?

_____

Find the perimeter of each figure.

10.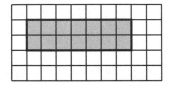

_____

11.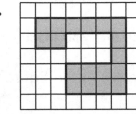

_____

12.

3 in. 5 in.

4 in.

_____

13.

5 cm

1 cm [   ] 1 cm

5 cm

_____

14.

9 cm

9 cm

_____

15.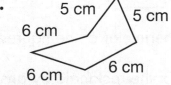

5 cm   5 cm

6 cm

6 cm   6 cm

_____

16. **Reasoning** If the length of one side of a square is 3 inches, what is the perimeter of the square? Explain your answer.

MDIS 2.0

Exploring Area

Use square pattern blocks to cover each shape. Write the number of squares you used.

1. ____ square units

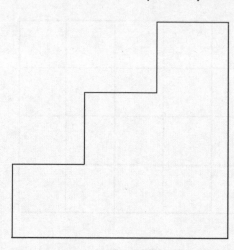

2. ____ square units

3. ____ square units

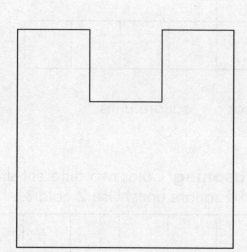

4. Color the shape with the greatest area red. Color the shape with the least area blue. How did you decide which shape had the greatest area?

142 (student p. 1)   MDIS 2.0

Name _____

Exploring Area (continued)

Find the area of each shape.

5.

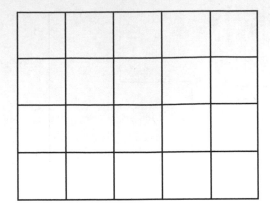

area: ___ square units

6.

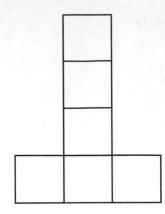

area: ___ square units

7.

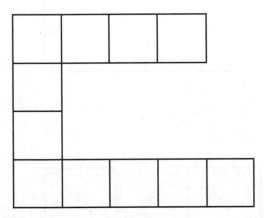

area: ___ square units

8.

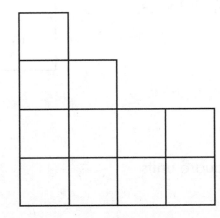

area: ___ square units

9. **Reasoning** Color two different shapes with an area
of 10 square units. Use 2 colors.

     MDIS 2.0

Finding Area on a Grid

Materials crayons or markers

Area is the number of square units needed to cover the region inside a figure.

Find the area of the rectangle by answering 1 and 2.

1. Color each grid square inside the rectangle. Count as you color. How many grid squares did you color? _____

2. What is the area of the rectangle?

   _____ square units

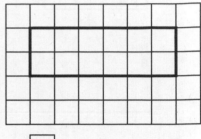

 = 1 square unit

Find the area of the polygon by answering 3 and 4.

3. Color each grid square inside the polygon. Count as you color. How many grid squares did you color? _____

4. What is the area of the polygon? _____ square feet

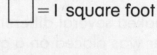 = 1 square foot

Estimate the area of the triangle by answering 5 to 8.

5. Color the whole squares blue. How many squares did you color? _____

6. Combine partial square to make whole squares. Color the partial squares red. The partial squares make up about how many whole squares? _____

7. Add. 6 + 3 = _____

8. What is the estimated area of the triangle?

   _____ square inches

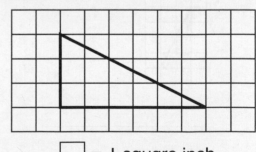

 = 1 square inch

 MDIS 2.0

Name _____

Finding Area on a Grid (continued)

Find each area. Write your answer in square units.

9.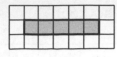

_____

_____

10.

_____

_____

11.

_____

_____

Find each area. Write your answer in square units.

12.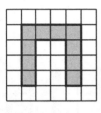

_____

13.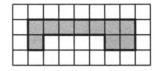

_____

14.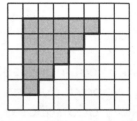

_____

Judy baked several different shapes of crackers and wants to know which is largest. Each cracker was placed on a grid. Estimate the area of each cracker in Exercises 15 to 17.

15. Triangle

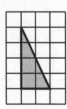

_____

_____

16. Hexagon

_____

_____

17. Quadrilateral

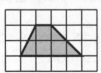

_____

_____

18. Which cracker in Exercises 15–17 has the greatest area?

143 (student p. 2) MDIS 2.0

More Perimeter

Jonah's pool is a rectangle. The pool is 15 feet long and 10 feet wide. What is the perimeter of the pool?

Find the perimeter of the pool by answering 1 to 3.

1. Write in the missing measurements on the pool shown at the right.

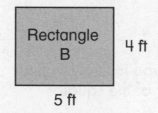

15 ft

10 ft _____ ft

_____ ft

2. Add the lengths of the sides.

10 ft + _____ ft + 15 ft + _____ ft = _____ ft

3. What is the perimeter of the pool? _____ ft

Find a formula for the perimeter of a rectangle by answering 4 to 10.

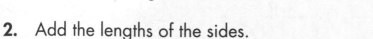

Rectangle A   3 in.

8 in.

Rectangle B   4 ft

5 ft

4. Write the side lengths of the rectangle.

8 + 3 + _____ + 3 = _____ in.

5. Rearrange the numbers.

8 + 8 + 3 + _____ = _____ in.

6. Rewrite the number sentence.

2(8) + 2 (_____) = _____ in.

16 + _____ = _____ in.

7. Write the side lengths of the rectangle.

5 + 4 + _____ + _____ = _____ ft

8. Rearrange the numbers.

5 + 5 + _____ + _____ = _____ ft

9. Rewrite the number sentence.

2(5) + 2(_____) = _____ ft

8 + _____ = _____ ft

10. Complete the table.

Rectangle	Length	Width	Perimeter
A	8		2(_____) + 2(3)
B			2(5) + 2(4)
Any	ℓ	w	$2\ell + 2$ _____

 MDIS 2.0

Name _____

More Perimeter (continued)

The formula for the perimeter of a rectangle is $P = 2\ell + 2w$

11. **Reasoning** Use the formula to find the perimeter of Jonah's pool.

$P =$ 2ℓ $+$ $2w$

$P = 2(\underline{\hspace{0.6cm}}) + 2(\underline{\hspace{0.6cm}}) = \underline{\hspace{0.8cm}} + \underline{\hspace{0.8cm}} = \underline{\hspace{0.8cm}}$ ft

12. Is the perimeter the same as you found on the previous page? _____

A square is a type of rectangle where all of the side lengths are equal.

Find a formula for the perimeter of the square by answering 13 to 15.

13. Add to find the perimeter of the square shown at the right.

$\underline{\hspace{0.8cm}} + \underline{\hspace{0.8cm}} + \underline{\hspace{0.8cm}} + \underline{\hspace{0.8cm}} = \underline{\hspace{0.8cm}}$

5 cm

14. What could you multiply to find
the perimeter of the square?   _____

15. If s equals the length of a side of a
square, how could you find the perimeter? $P = \underline{\hspace{0.8cm}}$

Find the perimeter of the rectangle with the given dimensions.

16. $\ell = 9$ mm, $w = 12$ mm   17. $\ell = 13$ in., $w = 14$ in.

_____   _____

18. $\ell = 2$ ft, $w = 15$ ft   19. $\ell = 17$ cm, $w = 25$ cm

_____   _____

Find the perimeter of the square with the given side.

20. $s = 2$ yd   21. $s = 10$ in.   22. $s = 31$ km   23. $s = 11$ m

_____   _____   _____   _____

24. **Reasoning** Could you use the formula for the perimeter of a rectangle to
find the perimeter of a square? Explain your reasoning.

    144 (student p. 2)   MDIS 2.0

Area of Rectangles and Squares

Maria's flower garden is in the shape of rectangle that measures 6 feet long and 4 feet wide. What is the area of the garden?

Find a formula for area of a rectangle by answering 1 to 6.

1. The rectangle at the right is a model of the garden. How many squares are in the model? _____

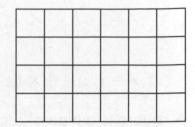

2. What is the area of the garden? _____ square feet

3. What is the length of the garden? _____ feet

4. What is the width of the garden? _____ feet

5. What could you multiply to find the area of the garden? _____

6. Find the area of each rectangle by counting squares. Write the area in the table below. Complete the table.

Rectangle A

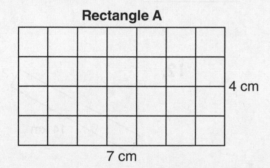

7 cm (bottom), 4 cm (right)

Rectangle B

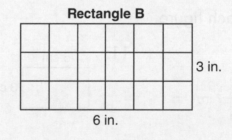

6 in. (bottom), 3 in. (right)

Rectangle	Area	Length	Width	Product
Maria's garden	24	6	4	6 × 4
A		7		7 × _____
B				_____ × _____
Any	Any	ℓ	w	ℓ × _____

MDIS 2.0

Name _____

Area of Rectangles and Squares (continued)

The formula for the area of a rectangle is $A = \ell \times w$ or $A = \ell w$.

7. **Reasoning** Use the formula to find the area of a rectangle that is 8 meters long and 5 meters wide.

$$A = \quad \ell \quad \times \quad w$$

$$A = (\_\_\_\_) \times (\_\_\_\_) = \_\_\_\_ \text{ square meters}$$

A square is a type of rectangle where all of the side lengths are equal.

Find a formula for the area of the square shown by answering 8 and 9.

8. Use the formula $A = \ell w$ to find the area of the square.

$$\_\_\_\_ \times \_\_\_\_ = \_\_\_\_ \text{ mm}^2$$

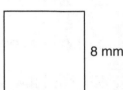

8 mm

9. If s equals the length of a side of a square, how could you find the area of any square? $A = _____$

Find the area of each figure.

10.
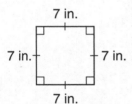
7 in.

7 in. — 7 in.

7 in.

11.
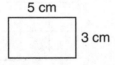
5 cm

3 cm

12.
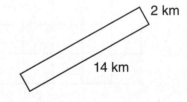
2 km

14 km

_____   _____   _____

Find the area of the rectangle with the given dimensions.

13. $\ell = 15$ mm, $w = 4$ mm

14. $\ell = 3$ cm, $w = 10$ cm

_____   _____

15. **Reasoning** The area of a square is 81 square feet. What is the length of each side?   _____

16. **Reasoning** Using only whole numbers, what are all the possible dimensions of a rectangle with an area of 12 square centimeters?

145 (student p. 2)   MDIS 2.0

Name _____

Area of Irregular Figures

Materials crayons or markers

Find the area of the irregular figure on the right.

1. How many squares are there? _____

2. What is the area of the figure? _____ square meters

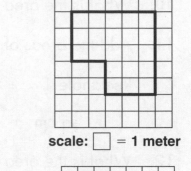

scale: ☐ = 1 meter

You can also find the area of the figure by breaking it into 2 rectangles and then finding the sum of the areas of the 2 rectangles.

3. What is the area of Rectangle 1?

    $A = \ell \times w$

    $A = 2 \times$ _____ = _____ sq meters

4. What is the area of Rectangle 2?

    $A = \ell \times w$

    $A = 3 \times$ _____ = _____ sq meters

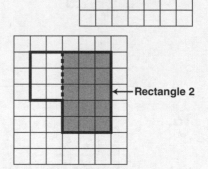

Rectangle 1 →

← Rectangle 2

5. What is the sum of the two areas?

    Area of Rectangle 1 + Area of Rectangle 2 = Total Area

         6   + _____   = _____ sq meters

6. Is the area the same as the one you found by counting? _____

Find the area of the shaded figure below by answering 7 to 12.

7. Divide the figure into 2 rectangles and a square.

8. What is the area of Rectangle 1?

    $5 \times$ _____ = _____ sq cm

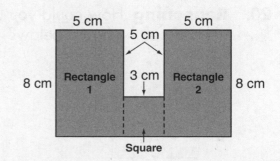

5 cm   5 cm

5 cm

8 cm   Rectangle 1   3 cm   Rectangle 2   8 cm

Square

        MDIS 2.0

Name _____

Area of Irregular Figures (continued)

9. What is the area of Rectangle 2? $5 \times$ _____ = _____ sq cm

10. What is the area of the square? $3 \times$ _____ = _____ sq cm

11. Add the areas of the three smaller figures.

Rectangle 1   +   Rectangle 2   +   Square   =   Total Area

_____ sq cm +   40 sq cm   +   _____ sq cm = _____ sq cm

12. What is the area of the figure? _____ sq cm

13.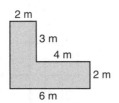

_____

14.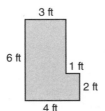

_____

15.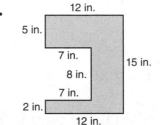

_____

16.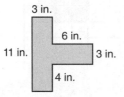

_____

17.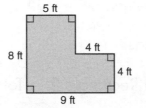

_____

18.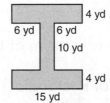

_____

19. Bob wants to carpet the room shown. How
many square yards of carpet will he need? _____

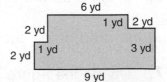

20. **Reasoning** How could you use subtraction to find
the area of the figure below?

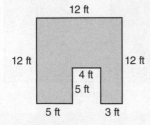

       MDIS 2.0

Name _____

Rectangles with the Same Area or Perimeter

Materials colored pencils or crayons.

Ms. Arellano's class is making a sand box shaped like a rectangle for the kindergarten class. They have 16 feet of wood to put around the sand box. What length and width should the sand box be so it has the greatest area?

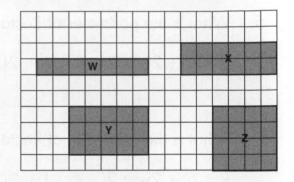

Each of the rectangles in the grid at the right has a perimeter of 16 feet. Find which rectangle has the greatest area by answering 1 to 3.

1. Complete the table. The formula for area of a rectangle is $A = \ell \times w$.

Rectangle	Length	Width	Area (square units)
W			
X			
Y			
Z			

2. What are the length and width of the rectangle with the greatest area? _____

3. What length and width should Ms. Arellano's class use for the sand box? _____

4. **Reasoning** Tracy told Tomas that if a two rectangles have the same perimeter, they have the same area. Is Tracy correct? Explain your reasoning.

Mr. Katz has 30 carpet squares to make a reading area in his classroom. Each square is one foot on a side. He wants to make the area in the shape of a rectangle with the least possible border. How should he arrange the carpet squares?

147 (student p. 1) MDIS 2.0

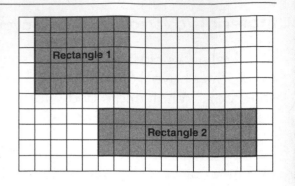

Name _____

Rectangles with the Same Area or Perimeter (continued)

Each of the rectangles on the grid at the right has an area of 30 square feet. Find which one has the least perimeter by answering 5 to 8.

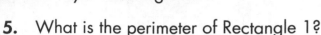

5. What is the perimeter of Rectangle 1?

   $P = 2\ell + 2w = 2(\underline{\quad}) + 2(5)$

   $= \underline{\quad} + \underline{\quad} = \underline{\quad}$ feet

6. What is the perimeter of Rectangle 2?

   $P = 2\ell + 2w = 2(\underline{\quad}) + 2(3) = \underline{\quad} + \underline{\quad} = \underline{\quad}$ feet

7. What is the length and width of the rectangle with the least perimeter?   _____

8. How should Mr. Katz arrange the carpet squares? _____

Draw a rectangle with the same area as the one shown. Then find the perimeter of each.

9.
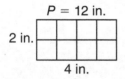
P = 12 in.
2 in.
4 in.

10.
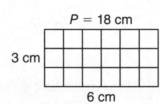
P = 18 cm
3 cm
6 cm

11.
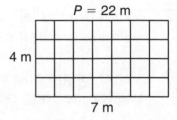
P = 22 m
4 m
7 m

_____   _____   _____

_____   _____   _____

12. **Reasoning** Marco has 36 feet of fencing, what is the greatest area that can he can fence?   _____

          MDIS 2.0

Name _____

Area of Parallelograms

Materials grid paper, colored pencils or markers, scissors

Find the area of the parallelogram on the grid by answering 1 to 10.

1. Trace the parallelogram below on a piece of grid paper. Then cut
    out the parallelogram.

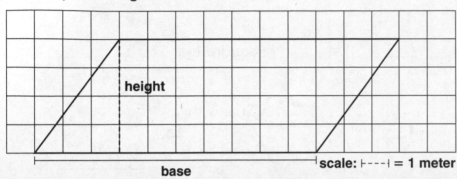

2. Cut out the right triangle created by the dashed line.

3. Take the right triangle and move it to the right of the parallelogram.

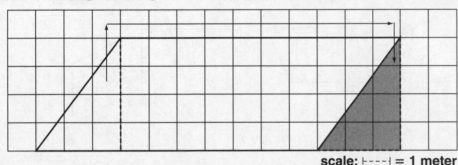

4. What shape did you create? _____

5. Is the area of the parallelogram the same as the area of the rectangle? _____

6. What is the area of the rectangle? $A = \ell \times w =$ _____ $\times\ 4 =$ _____ sq meters

7. What is the base b of the parallelogram? _____ meters

8. What is the height h of the parallelogram? _____ meters

9. What is the base times the height of the parallelogram? _____

10. Is this the same as the area of the rectangle? _____

148 (student p. 1)   MDIS 2.0

Name _____

Area of Parallelograms (continued)

The formula for the area of a parallelogram is $A = bh$.

11. Use the formula to find the area of a parallelogram with a base of
9 ft and a height of 6 feet.

$A =$ b × h

$A =$ (_____) × (_____) = _____ square feet

Find the area of each figure.

12.

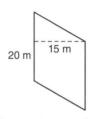

13.

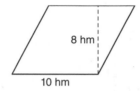

14.

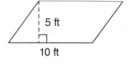

_____   _____   _____

15.

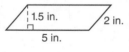

16.

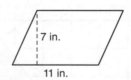

17.

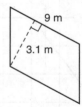

_____   _____   _____

18.

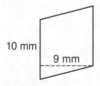

19.

20.

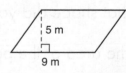

_____   _____   _____

21. Reasoning The area of a parallelogram is
100 square millimeters. The base is 4 millimeters.
Find the height.   _____

 MDIS 2.0

Name _____

Area of Triangles

Materials markers, crayons or colored pencils

Jerah is making a model of a sailboat. The sail of the boat is a triangle.
The sail has a base of 4 inches and a height of 3 inches. What is the
area of the sail? The triangle below. is a model of the sail.

Find the area of the sail by answering 1 to 5.

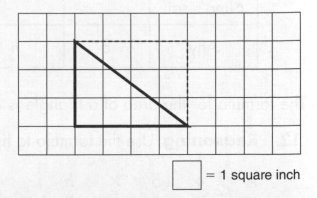

1. Color the triangle at the right.

2. How does the area of the triangle
   compare to the area of the rectangle?

   Area of the triangle = _____ × the
                                area of the rectangle

                                          = 1 square inch

3. What is the area of the rectangle? _____ square inches

4. What is the area of the triangle? _____ square inches

5. What is the area of Jerah's sail? _____ square inches

Nina is making a model of a sailboat with a sail in the shape of
a triangle like the one shown below. The base of her sail is
7 inches and the height is 4 inches. Find the area of the triangle
by answering 6 to 10.

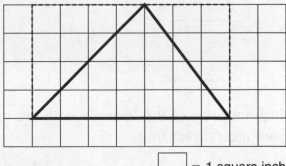

6. Color the triangle at the right.

7. How does the area of the triangle
   compare to the area of the rectangle?

   Area of the triangle = _____ × the
                                area of the rectangle

                                          = 1 square inch

8. What is the area of the rectangle? _____ square inches

9. What is the area of the triangle? _____ square inches

10. What is the area of Nina's sail? _____ square inches

      MDIS 2.0

Name _____

Area of Triangles (continued)

11. Complete the table.

Triangle	Base	Height	Area
Jerah's sail		3	
Nina's sail			
Any	b	h	$\frac{1}{2} \times b \times$ _____

The formula for the area of a triangle is $A = \frac{1}{2} \times b \times h$ or $A = \frac{1}{2}bh$.

12. **Reasoning** Use the formula to find the area of Jerah's sail.

$$A = \frac{1}{2} \times \quad b \quad \times \quad h$$

$$A = \frac{1}{2} \times \text{_____} \times \text{_____} = \text{_____ square inches}$$

13. Is the area the same as you found on the previous page? _____

Find the area of each figure.

14.

15.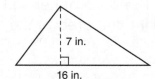

16.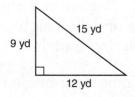

_____   _____   _____

Find the area of the triangle with the measurements shown below.
Give the correct units.

17. $b = 22$ yd
$h = 20$ yd

18. $b = 8$ mm
$h = 4$ mm

19. $b = 12$ cm
$h = 4$ cm

_____   _____   _____

20. The front of a tent is in the shape of a triangle with
a height of 6 feet and a base of 10 feet. What is the
area of the front of the tent?   _____

     MDIS 2.0

Name _____

Circumference

Materials Round objects, at least 3 for each group; tape measure or
ruler and string for each student

Circumference (C) is the distance around a circle.

1. Complete the table for 3 different round objects.

Object	Circumference (C)	Diameter (d)	c ÷ d

The last column should be close to π, ≈ 3.14, every time.

If $C \div d = \pi$, then $C = \pi d$.

2. What is the relationship between the diameter (d)
   and radius (r) of any circle? $d = $ _____

3. If $C = \pi d$ and $d = 2r$, what is a formula for
   the circumference using the radius (r)? $C = 2\pi$_____

Use a formula to find the circumference of each circle to the nearest
whole number.

4.

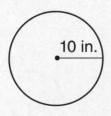

10 in.

$C = 2$　　π　　　r

$C \approx 2 \times 3.14 \times$ _____

$C \approx$ _____ inches

5.

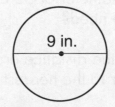

9 in.

$C = $　　π　　　d

$C \approx$ _____ $\times$ _____

$C \approx$ _____ inches

 MDIS 2.0

Name _____

Circumference (continued)

Find the circumference of each circle to the nearest whole number.
Use 3.14 or $\frac{22}{7}$ for π.

6.
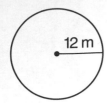
12 m

_____

7.
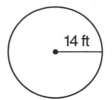
14 ft

_____

8.
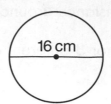
16 cm

_____

9.
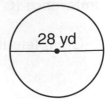
28 yd

_____

10.
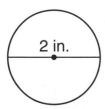
2 in.

_____

11.

13 mm

_____

12.
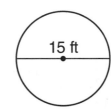
15 ft

_____

13.
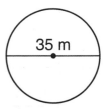
35 m

_____

14.
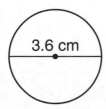
3.6 cm

_____

15.
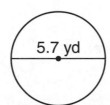
5.7 yd

_____

16.
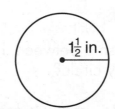
$1\frac{1}{2}$ in.

_____

17.
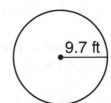
9.7 ft

_____

18. Miranda wants to sew lace around the outside of a pillow.
The pillow has a diameter of 35 centimeters. How much
lace does Miranda need?   _____

19. **Reasoning** Find the distance around the figure at the right.
Round your answer to the nearest whole number

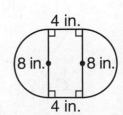
4 in.
8 in.   8 in.
4 in.

_____

20. **Reasoning** Write a formula for the circumference (C) of a semicircle.

_____

                    MDIS 2.0

Name _____

Area of a Circle

Materials crayons, markers, or colored pencils, grid paper, compass

Sue places a water sprinkler in her yard. It sprays water 5 feet in every direction. What is the area of the lawn the sprinkler waters?

Find a formula for the area of a circle and find the area of the lawn by answering 1 to 8.

1. The sprinkler sprays in a circle.
   What is the radius of the circle? _____

2. The grid at the right is a diagram of the sprinkler. Color all the whole squares within the circle one color. How many whole squares did you color?

   _____ whole squares

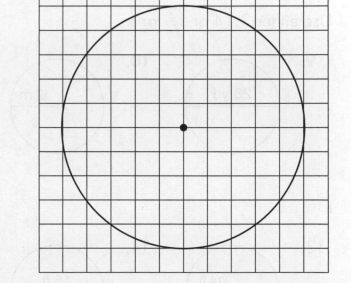

3. Combine partial squares to estimate whole squares. Color the partial squares, using a different color. The partial squares make up about how many whole squares?

   _____ whole squares

4. Add. What is a good estimate of the area of the circle? _____ units

5. Draw circles on grid paper with each radius listed in the table. Estimate the area and complete the table. Use 3.14 for π. Round πr^2 to the nearest whole number.

Estimated Area	Radius (r)	r^2	πr^2
80	5	25	
	3		28
	6		

6. Is the estimated area close to πr^2 each time? _____

 MDIS 2.0

Name _____

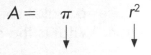

Area of a Circle (continued)

The formula for the area of a circle is $A = \pi r^2$.

7. Use the formula to find the area of a circle with radius 5 feet by filling in the blanks at the right. Round to the nearest whole number.

8. What is the approximate area of lawn watered by the sprinkler? Include the correct units.

    about _____

$A = \quad \pi \qquad r^2$

$\qquad\quad \downarrow \qquad\quad \downarrow$

$A \approx 3.14 \times$ _____

$A \approx$ _____

Find the area of each circle to the nearest whole number.
Use either 3.14 or $\frac{22}{7}$ for π.

9.
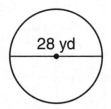
28 yd

10.
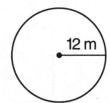
12 m

11.
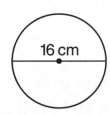
16 cm

12.
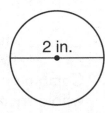
2 in.

_____   _____   _____   _____

13.
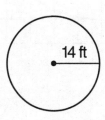
14 ft

14.
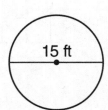
15 ft

15.
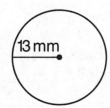
13 mm

16.
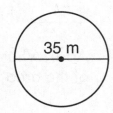
35 m

_____   _____   _____   _____

17. A cement ring the shape of a circle surrounds a flag pole. The ring is 6 meters across. How much sod, to the nearest whole square meter, does it take to cover the area inside the ring?   _____

18. **Reasoning** Chase used 3.14 for π and found the circumference of a circle to be 47.1 feet. Find the area of the circle to the nearest whole number.   _____

  MDIS 2.0

Name _____

Surface Area of Rectangular Prisms

Materials scissors, copy of nets for the square and rectangular prisms
from *Teaching Tool Masters,* for each student

The surface area of a rectangular prism is the sum of the areas of all
its faces.

How much wrapping paper does it take to cover the
box shown at the right, not counting overlap?

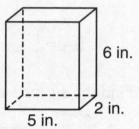

Find the surface area of the prism by answering 1 to 7.

1. Cut out and fold the net for a rectangular
    prism. Use the folded prism to write
    the length of each edge on the net.
    Use lengths shown in the prism
    above. Unfold the net and use it
    to label the lengths of the edges
    on the net at the right.

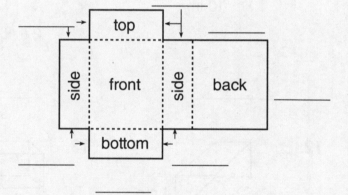

2. What is the area of the top
    and bottom of the prism?

    $5 \times 2 =$ _____ in.^{2}

3. What is the area of the side of the prism?

    _____ $\times$ _____ $=$ _____ in.^{2}

4. What is the area of the front and back of the prism?

    _____ $\times$ _____ $=$ _____ in.^{2}

5. Add the areas of all the faces to find the surface area.

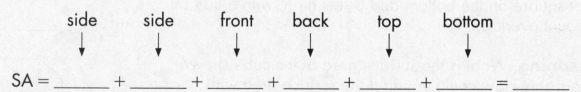

    SA $=$ _____ $+$ _____ $+$ _____ $+$ _____ $+$ _____ $+$ _____ $=$ _____

6. What is the surface area of the prism? _____ in.^{2}

7. How much wrapping paper does it take to cover the box? _____

152 (student p. 1)   MDIS 2.0

Surface Area of Rectangular Prisms (continued)

8. Cut out and fold the net for the square prism
and use it to find the surface area of the prism
at the right.

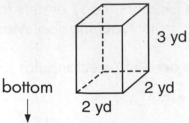
3 yd
2 yd
2 yd

side   side   front   back   top   bottom

↓   ↓   ↓   ↓   ↓   ↓

SA = _____ + _____ + _____ + _____ + _____ + _____ = _____ yd²

Find the surface area of each figure.

9.

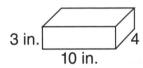
3 in. 4
10 in.

10.

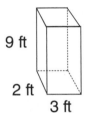
9 ft
2 ft
3 ft

11.

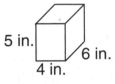
5 in. 6 in.
4 in.

_____   _____   _____

12.

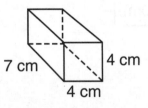
7 cm 4 cm
4 cm

13.

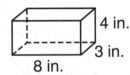
4 in.
3 in.
8 in.

14.

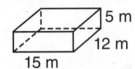
5 m
12 m
15 m

_____   _____   _____

15. What is the surface area of a rectangular prism that is 9 yards
wide, 10 yards long, and 11 yards high? _____

16. How much wood does it take to make a storage box that is
4 feet square on the bottom and 3 feet high, with a lid? Do
not count overlap. _____

17. **Reasoning** What is the surface area of the cube shown
at the right? How could you find the surface area with
out using addition?

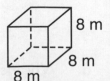
8 m
8 m
8 m

 MDIS 2.0

Surface Area

Materials scissors, copy of nets for the cylinder, square pyramid, and
triangular prism from *Teaching Tool Masters*, for each student

How much aluminum does it take to make a juice
can, not counting overlap, if the diameter is
6 centimeters and the height is 12 centimeters?

Find the surface area of a cylinder by answering 1 to 8.

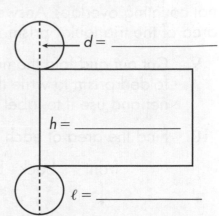

1. Cut out and fold the net for a cylinder. Use the
   folded cylinder to write the diameter and height
   of the can, on the net. Unfold the net and use it
   to label those dimensions on the net at the right.

In any prism or cylinder, the top and bottom are bases.
The remaining area is called the **lateral surface area**.

2. The lateral surface area of a cylinder makes a rectangle in the net. The
   width of the rectangle is the height of the cylinder. What is the length of the
   rectangle in the cylinder? Fold the net to see.

   The length of the rectangle = the _____ of the base.

3. Use the formula for the circumference of a circle to find the length of the
   rectangle. Write the length in the net above.

   $C = \pi d \approx$ _____ $\times$ _____ $\approx$ _____

4. What is the lateral surface area of the
   cylinder, to the nearest whole number?

   _____ $\times$ 18.84 $\approx$ _____

5. What is the radius of the base of the cylinder? $r =$ _____

6. What is the area of each base of the
   cylinder, to the nearest whole number?

   $A = \pi r^2 \approx$ _____ $\times$ _____ $\approx$ _____

7. What is the approximate surface area of the cylinder?

   base   base   lateral SA
    ↓   ↓   ↓

   SA $\approx$ _____ + _____ + _____ $\approx$ _____ cm²

153 (student p. 1)   MDIS 2.0

Name _____

Surface Area (continued)

8. How much aluminum does it take to make a juice can? _____

How much canvas does it take to make the pup tent shown, not counting overlap? Answer 9 to 12 to find the surface area of the triangular prism.

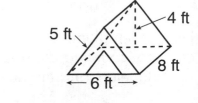

9. Cut out and fold the net for a triangular prism. Use the folded prism to write the lengths on the net. Unfold the net and use it to label the lengths on the net at the right.

10. Find the area of each face and write the areas below.

front   back   bottom   side   side

↓   ↓   ↓   ↓   ↓

SA = _____ + 12 + _____ + _____ + 40

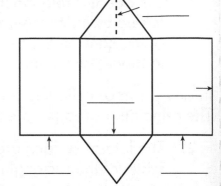

11. What is the surface area of the triangular prism? _____ ft²

12. How much canvas does it take to make the tent? _____

Answer 13 to 15 to find the surface area of the pyramid at the right.

13. Cut out and fold the net for a square pyramid to label the lengths on the net at the right.

14. Find the area of each face and write the areas below.

bottom   side   side   side   side

↓   ↓   ↓   ↓   ↓

SA = _____ + 60 + _____ + 60 + _____

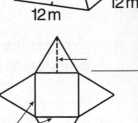

15. What is the surface area of the pyramid? _____

Find the surface area of each solid. Use 3.14 for π.

16.

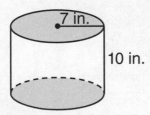

_____

17.

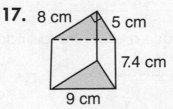

_____

18.

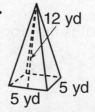

_____

   153 (student p. 2)

Counting Cubes to Find Volume

Materials 28 unit cubes for each student

Answer 1 to 10 to learn how to find the volume of a prism.

1. Build the rectangular prism on the right.

2. How many cubes did you use?

3. Build a second layer on the rectangular prism.

4. How many cubes did you
   use in the second layer?   _____

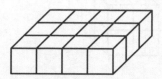

The **volume** of a figure is the number of
cubic units needed to fill it.

A **cubic unit** is a cube with edges that are 1 unit long.

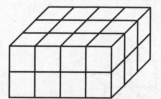

5. Find the total volume of the rectangular prism.

   cubes in 1st layer   +   cubes in 2nd layer   =   total cubes

   _____   +   _____   =   _____

6. What is the total volume of the
   rectangular prism?   _____ cubic units

7. Build a third layer on the rectangular prism by
   putting a row of cubes on top of the back row.

8. How many cubes did you
   use in the third layer?   _____

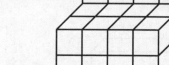

9. Find the total volume of the figure.

   cubes in   cubes in   cubes in
   1st layer   +   2nd layer   +   3rd layer   =   total cubes

   _____   +   _____   +   _____   =   _____

10. What is the total volume of the figure?   _____ cubic units

     MDIS 2.0

Name _____

Counting Cubes to Find Volume (continued)

Find the volume of each figure in cubic units.

11.
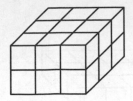

_____ cubic units

12.
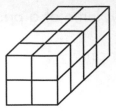

_____ cubic units

13.
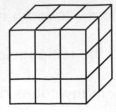

_____ cubic units

14.
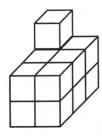

_____ cubic units

15.
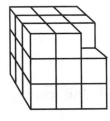

_____ cubic units

16.
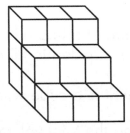

_____ cubic units

17. Reasoning Yao made a rectangular prism with 3 layers of cubes. He put 4 cubes in each layer. What is the volume of the rectangular prism?

_____ cubic units

18. Reasoning Box A consists of 8 cubic units. Three of Box A completely fills Box B. What is the volume of Box B?

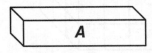

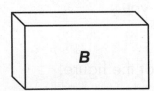

_____

 MDIS 2.0

Name _____

Measuring Volume

Materials 28 unit cubes for each student

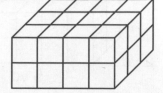

1. Build the rectangular prism on the right.

2. How many cubes did you use? _____

3. What is the volume? _____ cubic units

You can also find the volume (*V*) of a prism by multiplying
the length (ℓ) × width (*w*) × height (*h*).

4. Find the volume if each cube is 1 cubic foot.

    $V = ℓ \quad × \quad w \quad × \quad h$

    $V =$ _____ ft × _____ ft × _____ ft

    $V =$ _____ cubic feet

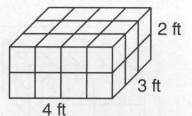

2 ft
3 ft
4 ft
1 cube = 1 cubic foot

5. Use cubes to find the volume of the prism
    at the right.

    $V =$ _____ cubic units

6. Use multiplication to find the volume.

    $V = ℓ \quad × \quad w \quad × \quad h$

    $V =$ _____ m × _____ m × _____ m

    $V =$ _____ cubic meters

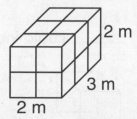

2 m
3 m
2 m
1 cube = 1 cubic meter

7. Find the volume of the prism at the right.

    $V = ℓ \quad × \quad w \quad × \quad h$

    $V =$ _____ in. × _____ in. × _____ in.

    $V =$ _____ cubic inches

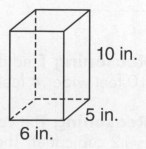

10 in.
5 in.
6 in.

 MDIS 2.0

Name _____

Measuring Volume (continued)

Find the volume of each figure.

8.

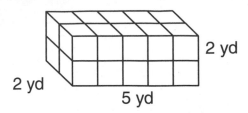

2 yd
2 yd
5 yd

_____ cubic yards

9.

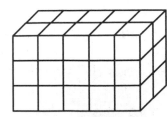

1 cube = 1 cubic centimeter

_____ cubic centimeters

10.

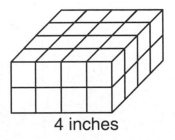

4 inches

_____ cubic inches

11.

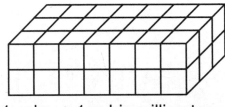

1 cube = 1 cubic millimeter

_____ cubic millimeters

12.

3 m
3 m
3 m

13.

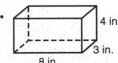

4 in.
3 in.
8 in.

14.

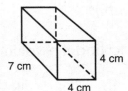

7 cm
4 cm
4 cm

15.

3 yd
2 yd
2 yd

_____

16. **Reasoning** Find the volume of a storage unit 10 feet wide, 4 feet long, and 4 feet high

17. **Reasoning** The volume of a rectangular prism is 12 cubic feet. The length is 6 feet and the width is 2 feet. What is the height?

_____ foot

 MDIS 2.0

Comparing Volume and Surface Area

Materials 24 unit cubes for each student

Kira's dad is making her a toy box in the shape of a rectangular prism.
The volume of the toy box is 24 cubic feet. He wants to know how
much outside area of the box he will need to paint.

The area which needs to be painted is the surface area of the box.
Find the surface area of a rectangular prism with a volume of 24 cubic
feet by answering 1 to 5.

1. Use 24 cubes to make a rectangular prism
   like the one shown at the right. If each cube
   represents a cubic foot, what is the volume
   of the prism? _____

2. You can find the surface area of a figure by finding the sum of the
   areas of each face of the figure. Complete the first row of the table
   for the prism you made.

Length	Width	Height	Area of Front and Back	Area of Sides	Area of Top and Bottom	Surface Area
4	3	2				
	2	2				

3. If Kira's dad makes the toy box 4 feet by 3 feet by 2 feet,
   how much outside area of the box will he need to paint? _____ ft²

4. Use the cubes to make a different rectangular prism with a volume
   of 24, a width of 2, and a height of 2. Use this prism to complete
   the second row of the table.

5. If Kira's dad makes the toy box 6 feet by 2 feet by 2 feet,
   how much outside area of the box will he need to paint? _____ ft²

The area Kira's dad needs to paint depends on the dimensions he uses.

6. **Reasoning** Why is the volume of the toy box given in cubic feet
   and the surface area given in square feet?

         MDIS 2.0

Name _____

Comparing Volume and Surface Area (continued)

Find the surface area and volume of each figure.

7.

_____

8.

_____

9.

_____

10.

_____

11.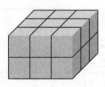

_____

12.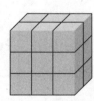

_____

13.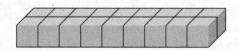

_____

14.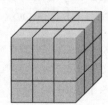

15. **Reasoning** Janet needs to determine how much wrapping paper she
needs to wrap three presents of the same size. Will she need to determine
the surface area or volume of the present? Explain.

 　　　　　　　　　MDIS 2.0

Recording Data from a Survey

Take a survey by asking, "What is your choice for a classroom mascot: a falcon, a cougar, a stingray, or a bear?"

1. Write each student's answer in the box below.

Choice of Classroom Mascot

2. Make a tally mark for each choice given. Remember, tallies are made in groups of 5 so that they are easier to count.

Sample of 12 Tally Marks

Choice of Classroom Mascot		
Mascot	**Tally**	**Total**
Falcon		
Cougar		
Stingray		
Bear		

3. Count the tally marks. Record the total for each mascot choice.

4. How many students answered the survey? _____

5. Which mascot was chosen the most? _____

6. Which mascot was chosen the least? _____

 MDIS 2.0

Recording Data from a Survey (continued)

Favorite Season of the Year					
Summer	Fall	Summer	Winter	Spring	Fall
Winter	Summer	Spring	Fall	Fall	Spring
Summer	Winter	Winter	Winter	Summer	Winter

7. Complete the tally chart for the data above.

Favorite Season of the Year		
Time of Year	**Tally**	**Total**

8. What was the question for the survey?

_____

9. How many people answered the survey? _____

10. Which season was the favorite of the most people? _____

11. Which season was the least favorite of the people? _____

12. How many more people chose Summer over Spring? _____

13. **Reasoning** Write the seasons in order from least favorite to most favorite.

_____

14. **Reasoning** How many more people would have to have chosen Summer for it to be the most favorite season? _____

 MDIS 2.0

Name _____

Reading and Making Pictographs

The members of Tom's class voted for their favorite pizza toppings. The results are shown in the tally chart at the right. Answer 1 to 7 to help you make and use a pictograph of the data.

Favorite Pizza Toppings		
Toppings	**Tally**	**Number**
Sausage	||||	4
Vegetables	|||	3
Pepperoni	|||| ||||	10

1. In the first row of the chart below write a title that best describes the pictograph. Then list the three toppings in the first column.

	◯◯
	◯◖

Each ◯ = 2 votes.   Each ◖ = _____ vote.

2. Complete the pictograph key.

3. Decide how many symbols are needed for each topping. Since sausage got 4 votes, draw 2 circles next to sausage. Since vegetables got 3 votes, draw 1 circle and 1 half-circle next to vegetables.

4. How many symbols are needed for pepperoni?   _____

5. Draw 5 circles for pepperoni. Make sure you line up the symbols.

6. Which topping got the greatest number of votes?   _____

7. **Reasoning** How can you tell which topping got the greatest number of votes by looking at the pictograph?

158 (student p. 1)   MDIS 2.0

Reading and Making Pictographs (continued)

For Exercises 8 to 11, use the
pictograph shown at the right.

Number of Fish in the Aquarium

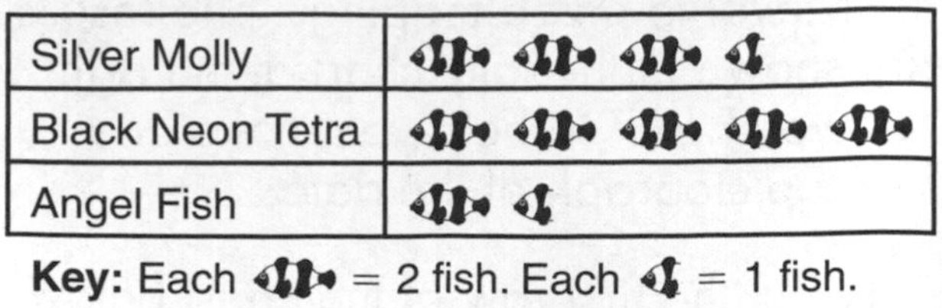

Silver Molly	⟨⟩ ⟨⟩ ⟨⟩ ⟨
Black Neon Tetra	⟨⟩ ⟨⟩ ⟨⟩ ⟨⟩ ⟨⟩
Angel Fish	⟨⟩ ⟨

Key: Each ⟨⟩ = 2 fish. Each ⟨ = 1 fish.

8. Which fish are there the
   most of in the aquarium?

   _____

9. How many Silver Molly fish are in the aquarium?   _____

10. How many more Black Neon Tetra fish
    are there than Angel Fish?   _____

11. Make a pictograph to display the data in the tally chart.

Favorite Drinks	
Fruit Juice	
Lemonade	
Milk	

Key: Each 🥛 stands for _____ votes.

Favorite Drinks		
Drinks	**Tally**	**Number**
Fruit Juice	⊞ III	8
Lemonade	⊞ ⊞ II	12
Milk	IIII	4

Use the pictograph you made in Exercise 11 to answer Exercises 12 to 15.

12. What does each 🥛 on the graph represent?

13. Which drink was chosen the least?   _____

14. How many more people chose lemonade over milk?   _____

15. **Reasoning** Do any kinds of drinks on the pictograph have the same
    number of votes? How do you know?

Name _____

Reading and Making a Bar Graph

Materials colored pencils, markers, or crayons, grid paper.

Robert's class voted for their favorite
country, not including the United States.
The results are shown in the table.

Make and use a bar graph of the data by
answering 1 to 6.

Our Favorite Countries	
Country	**Votes**
Canada	8
Great Britain	4
Japan	3
Mexico	11

1. Write a title above the graph. Label the
   axes: Country and Votes.

2. Complete the scale. Since the
   data go up to 11, make the
   scale by 2s.

3. Draw a bar for each country.
   Since Canada got 8 votes, color
   4 squares above Canada, up to
   the 8 mark. For Japan, color
   one and a half squares because
   3 is halfway between 2 and 4.

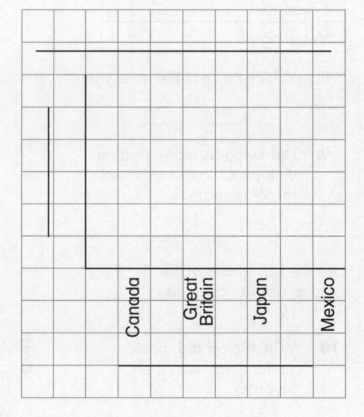

4. Which country got the least
   number of votes, that is,
   which has the shortest bar?

   _____

5. Which country got the greatest
   number of votes, that is,
   which has the longest bar?

   _____

6. **Reasoning** Which bar is twice as long as the bar for Great Britain? What
   does that mean?

 MDIS 2.0

Reading and Making a Bar Graph (continued)

Use the grid on the right for Exercises 7 to 9.

7. Draw a graph of the data
   in the table.

Cities We Want to See	
City	**Votes**
Anaheim	5
Orlando	12
Chicago	2
Washington	7

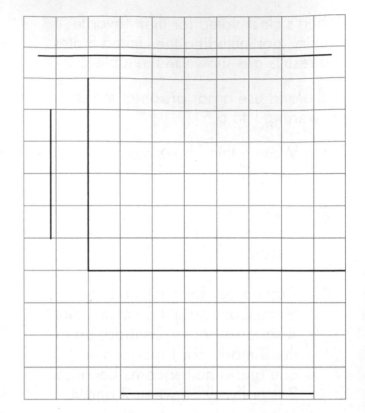

8. Which city got the most votes?

   _____

9. Did twice as many students
   vote for Orlando as voted
   for Washington?

   _____

Use the bar graph at the
right to answer Exercises
10 to 12.

10. Which craft did most
    students say was their
    favorite?

    _____

11. How many students chose
    boot making as their favorite
    craft demonstration? _____

12. How many more students chose wood carving than
    chose chair-caning as their favorite crafts? _____

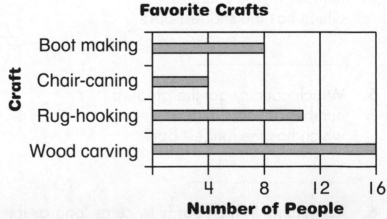

Favorite Crafts

Craft: Boot making, Chair-caning, Rug-hooking, Wood carving

Number of People
4   8   12   16

                 MDIS 2.0

Name _____

Making Line Plots

A year is sometimes divided into quarters, as show at the right.

1st quarter:	January to March
2nd quarter:	April to June
3rd quarter:	July to September
4th quarter:	October to December

1. Take a survey by asking, "Which quarter of the year were you born?" Write the number of the quarter each person answers in the grid.

2. What are all of the possible quarters that can be said?

**Quarter of the Year
You Were Born**

_____

Answer 3 to 7 to make and use a line plot of the data.

3. Draw a line. Below the line, list in order, all the possible quarters that could be said.

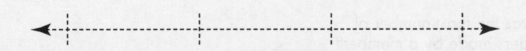

4. Write "Number of Birthdays by Quarter" below the line plot.

5. For each quarter that was said, mark an X above that quarter on the number line. If more than one X needs to be placed above a quarter, stack them in a single column.

6. Which quarter has the most number of birthdays? _____

7. How many birthdays are after the 2nd quarter? _____

 MDIS 2.0

Name _____

Making Line Plots (continued)

The nature club leader took a survey
of the number of birdfeeders each
member had made during camp.
The results are shown in the table.

**Birdfeeders Made
During Camp**

Member	Made	Member	Made
Ivan	4	Luther	5
Chloe	4	Marco	5
Stacey	3	Victoria	6
Victor	6	Chi	7
Tony	5	Wesley	5
Manny	6	Wendy	5

8. Make a line plot to show the data.

9. How many members made 4 birdfeeders? _____

10. How many members made 2 birdfeeders? _____

11. What was the most number of
    birdfeeders made by a member? _____

12. How many members made 5 or 6 birdfeeders? _____

13. How many members made less than 6 birdfeeders? _____

14. Did more members make more than
    5 birdfeeders or less than 5 birdfeeders? _____

15. **Reasoning** By looking at the line plot, if one more person
    attended camp, do you think that person would probably
    make 4 birdfeeders or 5 birdfeeders? Explain.

 MDIS 2.0

Name _____

Interpreting Graphs

Use the bar graph at the right to answer 1 to 9.

1. What is this bar graph about?

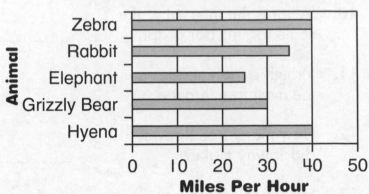

Maximum Speeds of Animals

The **scale** on a graph is the numbers used to describe the data.

2. The units used on this scale are miles per hour. What numbers does the scale use?

_____

The **interval** of the scale is the number you skip count by.

3. What is the interval of the scale? _____

4. Which animal has a maximum speed halfway between 20 and 30 miles per hour?

_____

5. What number is halfway between 20 and 30? _____

6. What is the maximum speed of an elephant? _____ miles per hour

7. Which animal has a maximum speed of 35 miles per hour? _____

8. Which animal(s) has a maximum speed that is 15 miles per hour greater than an elephant? _____

9. **Reasoning** Do any of the animals in the graph have a speed that is twice as fast as the elephant? How do you know?

 MDIS 2.0

Interpreting Graphs (continued)

For 10 to 13, use the graph on
the right.

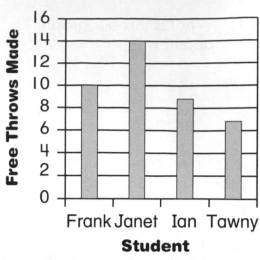

Free Throw Competition

10. What is the interval of the
    scale for this bar graph? _____

11. Which student made
    the most free throws? _____

12. How many free throws
    did Tawny make? _____

13. How many more free
    throws did Janet make
    than Ian? _____

For 14 to 18, use
the graph on the right.

National Park Visitation Poll

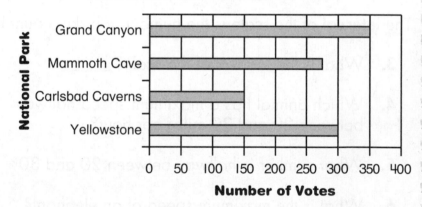

14. What is the interval
    of the scale?

    _____

15. Which park received
    275 votes?

    _____

16. Which park received twice as many
    votes as Carlsbad Caverns? _____

17. How many fewer votes did Carlsbad Caverns
    receive than the Grand Canyon? _____

18. **Reasoning** Which two parks received the closest number of votes?
    Explain how you know.

 MDIS 2.0

Name _____

Stem-and-Leaf Plots

The number of points earned on a history project, by each of nine students, are:

12, 27, 10, 18, 29, 12, 23, 12, 19

Answer 1 to 12, to make and use a stem-and-leaf plot of the data.

Make the **stem** the first digit of each number.

Points Earned	
Stem	**Leaves**
1	0
2	

1 | 8 = 18

1. What two stems are found in the data? _____

2. Write the stems, 1 and 2, in order from least to greatest under the heading Stem.

3. List all the numbers that have 1 as a stem.   _____

4. Write the numbers that have 1 as a stem in order from least to greatest.   _____

5. List all the numbers that have 2 as a stem.   _____

6. Write the numbers that have 2 as a stem in order from least to greatest.   _____

Make the **leaf** the second digit of each number. The leaves are listed in order from least to greatest after each stem.

7. Since 10 is the least number with a stem of 1, write a 0 after the stem 1. Since 12 is next, write 2 after the 0. Write the remaining leaves after the stem 1.

8. Since 23 is the least number with a stem of 2, write a 3 after the stem 2. Put this directly below the 0. Put 7 below the first leaf of 2 for 27 and 9 below the second 2.

9. What is the mode of the points earned data? _____

                   MDIS 2.0

Stem-and-Leaf Plots (continued)

---

10. What is the median of the points earned data? _____

11. What is the range of the points earned data? _____

12. What is the mean of the points earned data? _____

For Exercises 13 to 17 make a stem-and-leaf plot and then answer the questions. For one-digit numbers, use a zero in the stem.

13. Organize the data below for the pounds of newspapers collected by the classes for recycling into a stem-and-leaf plot:
6, 18, 12, 13, 11, 12, 12

14. Find the mean of the data. _____

15. Find the range of the data. _____

16. Find the median of the data. _____

17. Find the mode(s) of the data. _____

Use the stem-and-leaf plot on the right for Exercises 18 to 22.

18. What is the mode(s)? _____

19. What is the median? _____

20. What is the range? _____

21. What is the mean? _____

Length in Miles

Stem	Leaves
2	2 4
3	5 5 8 8 9

22. **Reasoning** How would the recycling stem-and-leaf plot from Exercise 13 change if the class that collected 6 pounds had collected 26 pounds?

MDIS 2.0

Histograms

Materials colored pencils

A **histogram** is a bar graph that has no space between the bars.
A histogram has equal intervals on the horizontal axis.

The table shows the ages of 25 people who attended a play. Complete the histogram based on the data given in the table by answering 1 to 9.

Age	Frequency
0–14	3
15–29	12
30–44	5
over 44	5

1. List the age intervals in each blank along the horizontal axis.

2. Label the scale along the vertical axis. Make each interval the same.

3. Give the graph a title and label the axes.

4. How many people were 14 and under? _____

5. Color a bar of height 3 above 0–14.

6. How many people were 15 to 29? Color a bar that height above 15–29. _____

7. How many people were 30 to 44? Color a bar that height above 30–44. _____

8. How many people were over 44? Color a bar that height above "over 44." _____

9. Did more people between the ages of 15 and 29 attend the play than people over 29? _____

MDIS 2.0

Histograms (continued)

The histogram shows the time, in minutes, that people who were surveyed spend driving to work. Use the graph for Exercises 10 to 13.

10. How many people were surveyed?

_____

11. How much time did 20% of the people surveyed spend driving to work?

_____

12. How much time did the most people spend driving to work?

_____

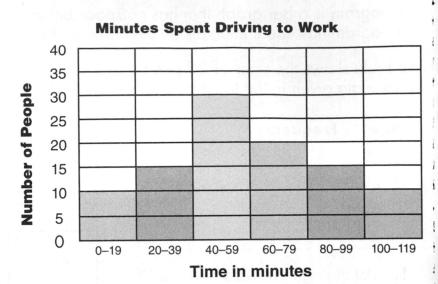

Minutes Spent Driving to Work

13. Reasoning Did twice as many of the people surveyed spend 40 to 59 minutes driving to work as spend 20 to 39 minutes? Explain how you can tell from the graph.

14. The table shows the results of a survey on the age of people visiting a restaurant. Use the data to complete the histogram.

Age	Frequency
0–19	12
20–39	18
40–59	10
60–79	4

Name _____

Finding the Mean

Materials color tiles: 5 red, 12 blue, and 7 yellow for each
student or group

The **mean,** or average, is the sum of all the numbers in a set of
data divided by the total number of data.

Carlos made 5 baskets in his first basketball game of the season,
12 baskets in the second game, and 7 in the third game.
What is the mean number of baskets that Carlos made during
the first three games?

Find the mean by answering 1 to 3.

1. Use tiles to represent the number of baskets that Carlos made. Make one
stack of 5 red tiles to represent the baskets in the first game, one stack of
12 blue tiles to represent the baskets in the second game and one stack of
7 yellow tiles to represent baskets in the third game.

2. Move tiles from one stack to another until there are three
stacks of equal height.

3. How many tiles are in each stack?   _____
This number represents the average number of baskets
in each game or the mean.

Find the mean without using tiles by answering 4 to 6.

4. What is the total number of baskets that Carlos
made in all three games? $5 + 12 + 7 =$ _____

5. If 24 tiles are divided between three stacks,
how many tiles are in each stack? $24 \div 3 =$ _____

6. Because there were 3 games, the total number of baskets
was divided by 3. This is the mean. Is this number the
same as the mean found when using the tiles?   _____

7. **Reasoning** Carlos scored no points in the fourth game of
the season. What effect does that have on the mean?

                                    MDIS 2.0

Name _____

Finding the Mean (continued)

Find the mean for each data set.

8. $120, $280, $410, $300, $180

_____

9. 175 ft, 136 ft, 157 ft, 112 ft

_____

10. 23 in., 37 in., 67 in., 93 in., 25 in.

_____

11. 5,341 km, 6,780 km, 2,543 km

_____

12. 89 weeks, 37 weeks, 27 weeks,
12 weeks, 86 weeks, 97 weeks

_____

13. 3 runs, 5 runs, 8 runs, 4 runs,
10 runs, 5 runs, 4 runs, 1 run

_____

14. $991, $759, $610, $967, $733

_____

15. 36 lb, 53 lb, 25 lb, 14 lb

_____

16. 76 bulbs, 36 bulbs, 98 bulbs,
25 bulbs, 38 bulbs, 27 bulbs

_____

17. 1,664 books, 2,533 books,
1,267 books, 7,668 books

_____

18. $67, $44, $32, $86, $12, $11

_____

19. 379 points, 255 points, 116 points

_____

20. $1,561; $2,689; $1,442;
$3,522; $1,756

_____

21. 4 h, 1 h, 0 h, 5 h, 7 h,
0 h, 5 h, 2 h

_____

22. Dale worked 7 days and made $350. What was the
average amount he made each day? _____

23. **Reasoning** Mrs. Hernandez's math class made the
following scores on a quiz: 5, 7, 8, 7, 9, 10, 2, 2, 3.
If 2 points are added to everybody's score, how is the
mean affected?

164 (student p. 2) MDIS 2.0

Name _____

Median, Mode, and Range

Materials 40-50 color tiles, counters or other small object
placed in a clear container

How many items are in the container? Collect your classmates'
guesses and find the median, mode, and range of the data by
answering 1 to 7.

1. Ask 9 people in your class to guess the number of items
   in the container. Write the 9 guesses in the blanks below.
   These numbers are the data.

   ___ ___ ___ ___ ___ ___ ___ ___ ___

The **median** is the middle number when the data are listed in order.

2. List the data in order from least to greatest. If there are
   some data that are the same, list those multiple times.

   ___ ___ ___ ___ ___ ___ ___ ___ ___

3. Circle the number that is in the middle of the list.
   What is the median of your data?   _____

The **mode** is the data value that occurs most often. If there is
more than one number that appears the most often, it is possible
to have more than one mode. If each number appears only once,
then there is no mode.

4. How many modes are there for your data?   _____

5. What is the mode of your data?   _____

The **range** is the difference between the greatest and least data values.

6. What is the difference between the greatest
   and the least data values?   _____

7. Count the number of items in the container.
   Was the median, mode, or range closest to the
   actual number of items?   _____

165 (student p. 1)   MDIS 2.0

Median, Mode, and Range (continued)

Find the median, mode and range of each data set.

8. 2, 5, 1, 8, 8, 12, 6

median _____

mode(s) _____

range _____

9. 25, 60, 20, 45, 25

median _____

mode(s) _____

range _____

10. 54, 54, 60

median _____

mode(s) _____

range _____

11. 4, 1, 1, 8, 8, 12, 8

median _____

mode(s) _____

range _____

12. 35, 23, 15, 23, 24

median _____

mode(s) _____

range _____

13. 15, 11, 12, 18, 14, 11, 9, 14, 13

median _____

mode(s) _____

range _____

14. If the number 8 were removed from the data in Exercise 11, what two numbers would be in the middle of the data? _____

The average, or mean, of 4 and 8 is the median. What is the median of the data after removing the number 8? _____

15. Reasoning If the number 100 is added to the data in Exercise 12, how does that affect the mean, median, mode, and range?

16. Brandi's scores on math exams were as follows: 96, 96, 89, 84, 25. Find the mean, median, and mode for Brandi's quiz scores.

17. Reasoning Which of the measures that you found in Exercise 16 best represents a typical exam score for Brandi? Explain.

 MDIS 2.0

Scatterplots

Amishi often sits in the park and counts butterflies. She makes a note of the number of minutes she sits outside and the number of butterflies she sees.

The table to the right shows the data she has collected.

Use this information to answer 1 through 7.

Number of Minutes	Number of Butterflies
2	1
5	3
8	4
17	8
25	12
29	17

1. How would you label the axes for a scatterplot of this data?

   x-axis: _____

   y-axis: _____

2. What is a reasonable scale and interval for the x-axis? Explain.

3. What is a reasonable scale and interval for the y-axis? Explain.

4. What would be a good title for the scatterplot?

   _____

5. Explain how to plot the points on the scatterplot.

6. Name two ordered pairs from the table.

   _____

7. Make a scatterplot of the data in the table.

         MDIS 2.0

Scatterplots (continued)

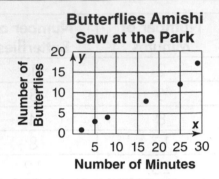

**Butterflies Amishi
Saw at the Park**

Use the scatterplot above to answer 8 through 13.

8. What is the trend shown in the scatterplot?

_____

9. What does the point (8, 4) represent?

_____

10. How many butterflies did Amishi see when she sat outside for 25 minutes?

_____

11. About how many more butterflies did she see in 29 minutes than she saw in 5 minutes?

_____

12. About how many butterflies do you think Amishi would see if she sat outside for 22 minutes?

_____

13. About how many butterflies do you think Amishi would see if she sat outside for 40 minutes?

_____

MDIS 2.0

Measuring Capacity or Weight

Jenna is going camping. She wants to bring a large pitcher so that she can make lemonade at the campsite.

She wants to make sure that the pitcher is not too heavy because she needs to carry it on the long walk to the campsite. And she needs to make sure it holds enough water to make lemonade for everyone.

Use this information to answer 1 through 6.

1. What does Jenna need to measure to make sure the pitcher is not too heavy to carry on the long walk, capacity or weight? How do you know?

2. What does Jenna need to measure to make sure the pitcher will hold enough water to make lemonade for everyone, capacity or weight? How do you know?

3. What unit might Jenna use to measure the weight of the pitcher?

_____

4. What are two different units that Jenna might use to measure the capacity of the pitcher?

_____

5. Karen carried a tent to the campsite. Jenna was curious to know how heavy the tent was, so Karen told her the weight. What units did Karen most likely use—ounces, pounds, or tons? Explain.

6. Jenna's friend Raud drove his truck to the campsite. The roof rack on the truck can safely hold up to 125 pounds. Raud wants to know whether he can carry a canoe on the roof rack. To decide, does he need to know the capacity or weight of the canoe? Explain.

 MDIS 2.0

Measuring Capacity or Weight (continued)

In 7 through 14, circle the correct answer.

7. Jack is making 3 quarts of chili. He wants to make sure that the pot he is using is large enough. Which is important for Jack to know?

The capacity of the pot   The weight of the pot

8. Maria drinks 8 glasses of water a day. She wants to know how much water she is actually drinking. Which should she measure?

The capacity of the glass   The weight of the glass

9. Gustav is filling a box with glass vases. He wants to make sure he can carry the box after it has been filled. What does Gustav need to know about each vase?

The capacity of each vase   The weight of each vase

10. Mr. Brook's class is doing a science experiment. They are using ounces as the measurement unit. What are they measuring?

Capacity   Weight

11. Kayla bought a 12-ounce bag of nuts. What does she know about the bag?

The capacity of the bag   The weight of the bag

12. Damian bought a sandbox for his children. He knows how much sand the sandbox can hold. What does he know about the sandbox?

The capacity of the sandbox   The weight of the sandbox

13. Juanita pours a quart of milk into a bowl and sees that the bowl is only half full. What is she measuring?

The capacity of the bowl   The weight of the bowl

14. Which unit would you use to measure the weight of a stack of pennies?

Pints   Ounces

 MDIS 2.0

Name _____

Solving Problems with Units of Time

Several friends signed up together for a creative writing class. This week's assignment is shown to the right.

Use this information to answer 1 through 4.

Creative Writing Class Weekly Assignment	
Write in your journal	40 minutes
Write a poem	15 minutes
Read short stories	25 minutes

1. Mariano has read a short story for 8 minutes. How much longer does he need to read? Show how to use a bar diagram to find the answer.

   _____

2. Alana has finished writing in her journal and writing a poem. How much time has she spent on her assignment? Show how to use a number line to find the answer.

   _____

3. Harrison wrote in his journal for 12 minutes in the morning. After lunch, he read short stories for 17 minutes. How many minutes has he worked on his assignments? Show how to use both a bar diagram and a number line to find the answer.

   _____

4. Olivia only has 9 more minutes of journal writing to do. How many minutes has she already spent writing in her journal? Show how to use a bar diagram to find the answer.

   _____

 MDIS 2.0

Solving Problems with Units of Time (continued)

For 5 through 13, solve each problem. You may use a bar diagram or number line to help you.

5. Tom tutors one student in math for 15 minutes. He tutors another student in science for 22 minutes. How long does he spend tutoring?

_____

6. The drive from Lowell to Norton is 55 minutes. Ruth has already driven 42 minutes. How many more minutes does she have to drive?

_____

7. Jada spends 18 minutes planting flowers in her garden. Then she takes a walk around the neighborhood for 23 minutes. Later that day, she plays tennis at the park for 15 minutes. How much time does she spend outdoors?

_____

8. Lisa napped for 37 minutes. Her sister Jody napped for 8 fewer minutes than Lisa. For how many minutes did Jody nap?

_____

9. Joy watches two cartoons. Each cartoon is 18 minutes long. How long does she watch cartoons?

_____

10. Gary walks for 35 minutes every day. He only has 11 more minutes to walk today. For how many minutes has he already walked?

_____

11. Cassie spends 45 minutes running three errands. It takes her 12 minutes to go to the post office. It takes her another 17 minutes to go to the grocery store. How long did it take her to run her third errand?

_____

12. Art class is 52 minutes long. Class began 19 minutes ago. How many more minutes does art class last?

_____

13. Molly is playing math games on the computer. She plays one math game for 28 minutes, and she plays another math game for 29 minutes. How many minutes does Molly play math games on the computer?

_____

 MDIS 2.0

Making Dot Plots

Adella invited 22 friends to her birthday party. The table shows the ages of her friends at the party.

Use this information to answer 1 through 7.

Adella's Birthday Party	
Age	Number of Friends
8	4
9	8
10	6
11	3
12	1

1. What is a reasonable scale for a dot plot of the data in the table? How do you know?

2. What would be a good title for the dot plot?

3. How can you make a dot plot of the data in the table?

4. Make a dot plot for the data in the table.

5. What is the age of the youngest friend at the party? _____

6. What is the age of the oldest friend at the party? _____

7. What is the most common age at Adella's party? _____

Making Dot Plots (continued)

Ms. Gold's English class had a contest to see how many books students could read over the summer. 1 student read 2 books. 5 students read 4 books. 9 students read 5 books. 6 students read 6 books. 3 students read 7 books. 2 students read 9 books.

Use this information to answer 8 through 15.

8. What is a reasonable scale for a dot plot of this data?

9. Make a dot plot for the data.

10. How many students read 4 books? _____

11. How many students read 8 books? _____

12. What was the most common number of books read? _____

13. What was the least number of books read by a student? _____

14. What was the greatest number of books read by a student? _____

15. How many students read 7 or more books? _____

Name _____

Converting Units

Mandy brought 1.75 gallons of lemonade to the picnic.
Answer the following to find how many one-cup servings
she can make.

1. It takes 16 cups to equal a gallon. Complete the conversion factor.

$$\frac{\boxed{} \text{ c}}{\boxed{} \text{ g}}$$

2. Write an equivalent rate.

$$\frac{\boxed{} \text{ c} \times 1.75}{\boxed{} \text{ g} \times 1.75} = \frac{\boxed{} \text{ c}}{1.75 \text{ g}}$$

3. Mandy can make _____ one-cup servings.

Juan brought a 6-pack of juice bottles to the picnic.
Each bottle holds 10 fluid ounces of juice. Answer the
following to find how many one-cup servings he can make.

4. Juan brought _____ fluid ounces of juice in all.

5. It takes 8 fluid ounces to equal a cup. To write
an equivalent rate like the one at the right, think:
What times 8 equals 60? Solve $8n = 60$.

$$\frac{1 \text{ c}}{8 \text{ fl oz}} = \frac{\boxed{} \text{ c}}{60 \text{ fl oz}}$$

$8n = 60$

$\dfrac{8n}{8} = \dfrac{60}{8}$

$n =$ _____

6. Write an equivalent rate.

$$\frac{1 \text{ c} \times \boxed{}}{8 \text{ fl oz} \times \boxed{}} = \frac{\boxed{} \text{ c}}{60 \text{ fl oz}}$$

7. Juan can make _____ one-cup servings.

 MDIS 2.0

Converting Units (continued)

George brought 2.25 pounds of hamburger to the picnic. Answer the following to find how many four-ounce servings he can make.

8. It takes 16 ounces to equal a pound. Use dimensional analysis to find how many ounces are in 2.25 lb.

$$\boxed{}\ \text{lb} \times \frac{\boxed{}\ \text{oz}}{1\ \text{lb}} = \boxed{} \times \boxed{}\ \text{oz} = \boxed{}\ \text{oz}$$

2.25 lb = _____ oz

9. George can make _____ four-ounce servings.

Kara brought a 42-inch long sandwich to the picnic. Answer the following to find how many feet long the sandwich is.

10. It takes 12 inches to equal a foot. Use dimensional analysis to find how many feet are in 42 inches.

$$\boxed{}\ \text{in.} \times \frac{\boxed{}\ \text{ft}}{\boxed{}\ \text{in.}} = \frac{\boxed{}}{\boxed{}}\ \text{ft} = \boxed{}\ \text{ft}$$

11. Kara's sandwich is _____ feet long.

Find how many quarts equal 7.5 pints, using each method.

12. Use equivalent ratios.

$$\frac{1\ \text{qt}}{2\ \text{pts}} =$$

13. Use dimensional analysis.

14. **Reasoning** Lexie said that it is easier to use dimensional analysis to change 7.5 pints to quarts. Tomas said it is easier to use equivalent ratios. What do you think? Explain.

MDIS 2.0

Name _____

Line Plots

Materials: inch ruler for each student

Twelve fifth grade students measured their
hand spans to the nearest one fourth inch.
The table shows the measures they got.

Widths of Hand Spans in Inches			
$6\frac{1}{2}$	$6\frac{3}{4}$	$5\frac{3}{4}$	$5\frac{1}{4}$
$7\frac{1}{2}$	$6\frac{1}{2}$	$6\frac{3}{4}$	$6\frac{1}{4}$
$6\frac{1}{4}$	$7\frac{1}{4}$	6	$6\frac{3}{4}$

1. What is a reasonable scale for a line plot of
    the data in the table? How do you know?

2. Make a line plot of the data in the table.

    _____

    |←|————————————————————|→|

Use the line plot you made to answer the questions.

3. Which width occurred the most often?
    How can you use the line plot to tell?

4. How many students had a hand span of $6\frac{1}{4}$ inches? _____

5. What is the difference between the greatest hand
    span and the least hand span? Show how you solve.

       MDIS 2.0

Line Plots (continued)

The twelve students also measured the length
of their index fingers to the nearest $\frac{1}{8}$ of an inch.
The table shows the measures they got.

Lengths of Index Fingers in Inches			
$2\frac{1}{2}$	$2\frac{3}{8}$	$2\frac{3}{4}$	$1\frac{7}{8}$
$1\frac{5}{8}$	$2\frac{5}{8}$	$2\frac{3}{8}$	$2\frac{1}{4}$
$2\frac{1}{4}$	2	$2\frac{3}{4}$	$2\frac{3}{8}$

6. What is a reasonable scale for a line plot
    of the data in the table? How do you know?

7. Make a line plot of the data in the table.

    _____

    ◄———————————————————————►

Use the line plot you made to answer the questions.

8. Which length occurred the most often?   _____

9. What is the difference between the greatest length
    and the least length?   _____

10. **Reasoning** Tessa said that the combined length of all 5
    of her fingers on one hand should be less than 5 times the
    length of her index finger. Tessa had the second shortest
    index finger. The combined length of all 5 of her fingers
    is less than what length? Show how you solved.

MDIS 2.0

Combining Volumes

Nabeel's room has a window seat. A model of his
room is shown.

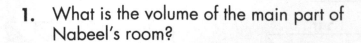

1. What is the volume of the main part of
   Nabeel's room?

   $V = \quad l \quad \times \quad w \quad \times \quad h$

   $V = $ _____ $\times$ _____ $\times$ _____ $=$ _____ cubic feet

2. What is the volume of the window seat?

   $V = \quad l \quad \times \quad w \quad \times \quad h$

   $V = $ _____ $\times$ _____ $\times$ _____ $=$ _____ cubic feet

3. What is the total volume of Nabeel's room?

   _____ $+$ _____ $=$ _____ cubic feet

4. Tariq used cardboard boxes to
   build a playhouse for his little sister.
   The dimensions of the boxes
   are shown. What is the volume
   of the playhouse?

   Big Box: $V = l \times w \times h$

   $V = $ _____ $\times$ _____ $\times$ _____ $=$ _____ cubic inches

   Little Box: $V = l \times w \times h$

   $V = $ _____ $\times$ _____ $\times$ _____ $=$ _____ cubic inches

   Total volume: _____ $+$ _____ $=$ _____ cubic inches

MDIS 2.0

Combining Volumes (continued)

Find the volume of each solid figure. Show your work.

5. V = _____

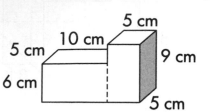

6. V = _____

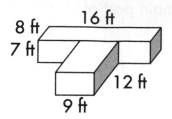

7. V = _____

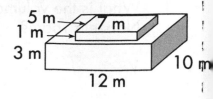

8. What is the volume of the jewelry box shown? Show your work.

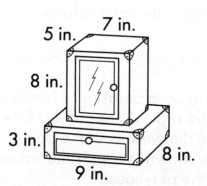

9. **Reasoning** Which solid has a greater volume? Explain how you can tell without calculating.

Solid A

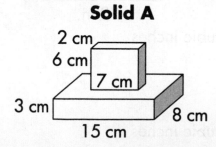

Solid B

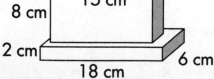

MDIS 2.0

Polygons on the Coordinate Plane

Henry's mother is planning a new city park.
The park will be in the shape of a polygon with
vertices at $(-4, 3)$, $(3, 3)$, $(3, -4)$, and $(-4, -2)$.

1. Draw a diagram of the park. Graph the points
on the coordinate grid and then connect them
to form a polygon. Label the points with their
coordinates.

2. The distance between $(-4, 3)$ and $(3, 3) =$

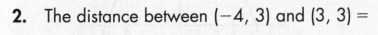

3. The distance between $(-4, 3)$ and $(-4, -2) =$

4. The distance between $(3, 3)$ and $(3, -4) =$

5. Draw a dashed line to divide the polygon into a rectangle
and a triangle. Find the area of the rectangle. Use the
distances you found for the lengths of the sides.

$A = l \cdot w$

$= \underline{\hspace{1.5cm}} \cdot \underline{\hspace{1.5cm}} = \underline{\hspace{1.5cm}}$ m^2

6. How can you find the height of the triangle?

_____

7. Find the area of the triangle.

$A = \frac{1}{2} \cdot b \cdot h$

$= \frac{1}{2} \cdot \underline{\hspace{1.5cm}} \cdot \underline{\hspace{1.5cm}} = \underline{\hspace{1.5cm}}$ m^2

8. What is the area of the park?

$\underline{\hspace{1.5cm}} + \underline{\hspace{1.5cm}} = \underline{\hspace{1.5cm}}$ m^2

 MDIS 2.0

Polygons on the Coordinate Plane (continued)

Find the area of each polygon. Explain how you found
the area.

9. A = _____

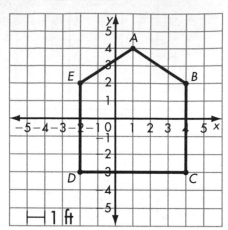

10. A = _____

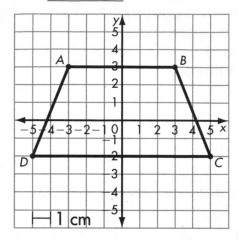

11. Reasoning Kenna is designing a headscarf
for her doll on a coordinate grid. The scarf
will be in the shape of a polygon with
vertices at $(-2, 4)$, $(2, 4)$, $(4, 1)$, and $(-4, 1)$.

- Graph these points on the grid.
- Draw dashed lines to divide the polygon
  into rectangles and triangles.
- Show how to find the area of each part and
  the total area.

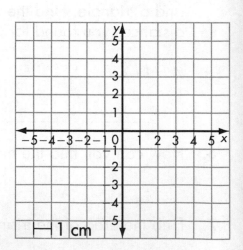

                    MDIS 2.0

Statistical Questions

The sixth grade class is taking a survey about colors. They need to ask a statistical question, one where they can expect to get different answers.

Decide whether or not the following is a statistical question.

What are the primary colors?

1. Would people give the same or different answers to this question? Explain.

2. Is this a statistical question?   _____

Decide whether or not the following is a statistical question.

What is your favorite color?

3. Would people give the same or different answers to this question? Explain.

4. Is this a statistical question?   _____

You can expect variability in the answers to a statistical question.
The answers vary from one person to another.

Decide whether or not each of the following is a statistical question.
Explain your answer for each.

5. What color are the walls in your math classroom?

6. How many colors do you have in your wardrobe, that is, in the clothes you wear?

 MDIS 2.0

Name _____

Statistical Questions (continued)

Choose a book to use. Answer the following questions.

7. How many words are in a paragraph? Give the count for 6 paragraphs.

_____

8. How many words are in the title?

_____

Explain your answer for each.

9. Is the question in Exercise 7 statistical?

10. Is the question in Exercise 8 statistical?

11. Would it make more sense to draw a graph of the data in Exercise 7 or the data in Exercise 8? Justify your answer.

12. Reasoning Write a statistical question you could ask people in your class.

13. Ask 10 people your statistical question and list the answers here. Make a bar graph of the results.

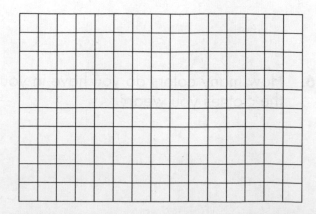

 MDIS 2.0

Box Plots

Nine students measured the length of one hair on their
heads to the nearest inch. They got the following results.

4, 8, 0, 1, 4, 0, 3, 2, 5

1. Write the numbers in the boxes below, in order from least to greatest.

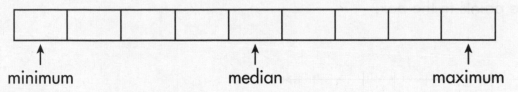

minimum   median   maximum

2. The least number is the minimum. What is the
minimum hair length?   _____ in.

3. The greatest number is the maximum. What is
the maximum hair length?   _____ in.

4. The median is the middle number when the data
are listed in order from least to greatest. What is
the median hair length?   _____ in.

5. Write the numbers that are below the median
in the boxes. Keep them in order from least to
greatest.

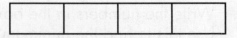

Remember, to find the median of an even number of data
values, you find the average of the two middle numbers.

6. What is the median of the numbers in Exercise 5, in decimal form?

$$\frac{\boxed{} + \boxed{}}{2} = \frac{\boxed{}}{2} = \boxed{}$$

This is the first quartile. It is the median of the numbers below
the median of the data set.

7. The third quartile is the median of the numbers above
the median of the data set. What is the third quartile?

$$\frac{\boxed{} + \boxed{}}{2} = \frac{\boxed{}}{2} = \boxed{}$$

                                        MDIS 2.0

Box Plots (continued)

8. Draw a box plot of the hair length data. Follow these steps.

   • Use a number line with an appropriate scale, like the one below.
   • Draw a box between the first and third quartiles.
   • Draw a vertical line in the box at the median.
   • Put points at the minimum and maximum values and draw segments from these points to the box.

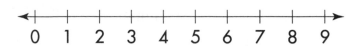

0 1 2 3 4 5 6 7 8 9

The box plot divides the data into fourths. So, $\frac{1}{4}$ or 25% of the data is between 0 and 0.5. Another 25% is between 0.5 and 3, another between 3 and 4.5, and another between 4.5 and 8.

Ten students counted how many times their hearts beat in 15 seconds. They got the following results.

   15, 18, 14, 21, 18, 20, 16, 19, 16, 16

9. Write the numbers in the boxes below, in order from least to greatest. Use this to find the minimum, maximum, median, and the first and third quartiles.

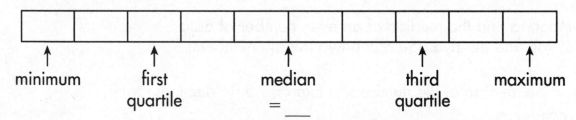

minimum   first   median   third   maximum
              quartile   = ___   quartile

10. **Reasoning** Draw a box plot of the heartbeat data.

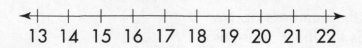

13 14 15 16 17 18 19 20 21 22

175 (student p. 2)   MDIS 2.0

Name _____

Measures of Variability

The girls on the middle school basketball team have
the following heights, in inches.

59, 61, 57, 58, 60, 59, 58, 60, 62, 56

1. What is the mean height? _____

2. Complete the table to find the difference
between each data value and the mean.

3. What is the mean of these differences?
Show your work.

Score	Absolute Deviation
56	$\lvert 59 - 56 \rvert =$
57	$\lvert 59 - 57 \rvert =$
58	$\lvert 59 - 58 \rvert =$
58	$\lvert 59 - 58 \rvert =$
59	$\lvert 59 - 59 \rvert =$
59	$\lvert 59 - 59 \rvert =$
60	$\lvert 60 - 59 \rvert =$
60	$\lvert 60 - 59 \rvert =$
61	$\lvert 61 - 59 \rvert =$
62	$\lvert 62 - 59 \rvert =$

This is the mean absolute deviation (MAD).
It is a measure of variability. Since the MAD
is a small number, it indicates that the heights
of the girls on the team do not vary much. They
are all close to the same height.

4. Write the heights in the boxes below, in order from
least to greatest. Use this to find the minimum,
maximum, median, and the first and third quartiles.

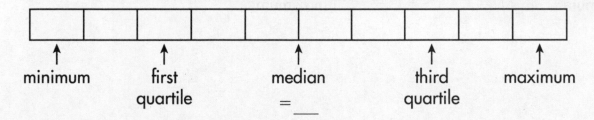

minimum   first   median   third   maximum
           quartile   = ___   quartile

5. Draw a box plot of the height data.

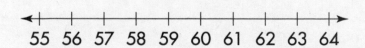

   176 (student p. 1)   MDIS 2.0

Measures of Variability (continued)

6. What is the difference of the first and third quartiles? _____

This is the interquartile range (IQR). It is also a measure of variability. Like the MAD, the IQR indicates that the heights do not vary much.

7. What percent of the heights are within an interval equal to the IQR? _____

In the first 6 games, the basketball team scored the following numbers of points.

25, 30, 45, 26, 32, 28

8. What is the mean absolute deviation? Explain how you found it. _____ points

Score	Absolute Deviation

9. What is the interquartile range? Explain how you found it. _____ points

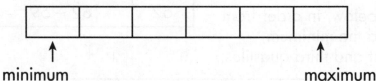

minimum   maximum

10. **Reasoning** Does the outlier 45 have more effect on the MAD or the IQR? Justify your answer.

 MDIS 2.0

Name _____

Appropriate Use of Statistical Measures

Two teams of sixth grade students had a contest to see which team could type the most words on a computer keyboard in 15 seconds. Each team had 10 members. The results are shown in the table.

Words Typed										
Rockets	7	8	6	9	10	20	6	7	7	5
Pacers	11	12	9	8	7	8	12	8	7	8

1. What is the mean number of words the Rockets typed? Show your work.

2. What is the median number of words the Rockets typed? _____

3. Does the mean or the median give a better indication of the typical number of words the Rockets typed? Justify your answer.

4. What is the mean number of words the Pacers typed? Show your work.

5. What is the median number of words the Pacers typed? _____

6. Does the mean or the median give a better indication of the typical number of words the Pacers typed? Justify your answer.

When the median is the best measure of center, use the interquartile range (IQR) to measure the variability. When the mean is the best measure of center, use the mean absolute deviation (MAD) to measure variability.

7. What is the IQR for the number of words the Rockets typed? _____

MDIS 2.0

Appropriate Use of Statistical Measures (continued)

8. What is the MAD for the number of
words the Pacers typed? Use the table
to help you find it.

MAD = _____

9. The MAD for the Rockets is 2.7. Which
team had more variability in the number of
words the members typed?

_____

Words	Absolute Deviation

The table shows the
speeds of 5 practice
serves by two tennis
players.

Serve Speed (in mph)					
Joe	46	50	49	52	48
Andy	45	60	50	47	43

10. What is the mean speed of
Joe's serves?

_____

11. What is the median speed
of Joe's serves?

_____

12. What is the mean speed of
Andy's serves?

_____

13. What is the median speed
of Andy's serves?

_____

14. Who has a faster serve on average, Joe or Andy?
Use a measure of center to justify your answer.

15. Does the mean or the median give a better indication
of the typical speed of Andy's serves? Explain.

16. **Reasoning** Whose serve is more consistent? Use
IQR to justify your answer.

     MDIS 2.0

Name _____

Summarize Data Distributions

A data distribution is how the values are arranged in a data set.
To describe a data distribution you:

- give a measure of center,
- give a measure of variability,
- describe the overall shape of the data, and
- sometimes show the data in a graph.

Eight students each shot 20 basketball free throws. The list
shows how many free throw shots they made.

10, 9, 8, 10, 15, 5, 9, 14

1. What is the mean number of free throws the players made?
   Show your work.

2. Write the data in the boxes below, in order from least to greatest. Use this
   to find the minimum, maximum, median, and the first and third quartiles.

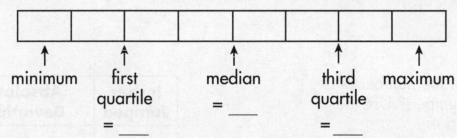

Since the mean and the median are close, either one is appropriate.

3. Draw a box plot of the free throw data.

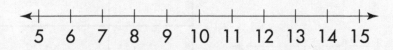

4. What is the IQR for the number of free throws
   the students made?   _____

                       MDIS 2.0

Name _____

Summarize Data Distributions (continued)

5. Describe the overall shape of the data by answering the following questions.

   • Are the data values symmetric or more spread out to either the right or the left?
   • Are there any gaps in the data?
   • Where are most of the data values grouped?

Eight students did a standing high jump. The data show how far they jumped, in inches.

16, 11, 19, 10, 16, 21, 12, 15

Describe the data distribution by answering the following.

6. What is the mean number of inches the students jumped? Show your work.

7. What is the MAD for the number of inches the students jumped? Use the table to help you find it.

   MAD = _____

Inches Jumped	Absolute Deviation

8. Make a dot plot of the data to help you see the overall shape of the distribution.

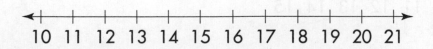

9. **Reasoning** Describe the overall shape of the data distribution.

 MDIS 2.0